$$\frac{156 - 2EB.}{320} \quad 382 \enspace ③$$

AN
INTRODUCTION
TO
KINESIOLOGY

Prentice-Hall Foundations of Physical Education Series

JOHN E. NIXON
Stanford University
Series Editor

AN
INTRODUCTION
TO
KINESIOLOGY

Marion R. Broer

Ph.D.
University of Washington

With
Contributions by

S. J. Houtz

M.S.
Detroit Orthopaedic Clinic

PRENTICE-HALL, INC., ENGLEWOOD CLIFFS, NEW JERSEY

Drawings in the text by

Diann Laing

University of Washington

PRENTICE-HALL INTERNATIONAL, INC., *London*
PRENTICE-HALL OF AUSTRALIA, PTY. LTD., *Sydney*
PRENTICE-HALL OF CANADA, LTD., *Toronto*
PRENTICE-HALL OF INDIA PRIVATE LTD., *New Delhi*
PRENTICE-HALL OF JAPAN, INC., *Tokyo*

Series Preface

The purpose of the *Foundations of Physical Education* series is to provide a set of textbooks which, by presenting selected generalizations from related fields of knowledge, contribute to a sophisticated understanding of physical education as an academic discipline. These validated generalizations provide a sound basis for educational decision-making by teachers, coaches, supervisors, and administrators at all school levels.

Physical education currently is defined as the art and science of voluntary, purposeful human movement. Its central concern is man engaging in selected motor performances and the meaning and significance of these experiences. Thus, physical education is a broad cross-disciplinary subject. It requires of its scholars and practitioners a command of the most relevant generalizations, being generated in the closely related disciplines, which describe and explain phenomena associated with human movement. Those disciplines which provide the most relevant foundational knowledge for physical education are physiology, neurology, psychology, sociology, anthropology, history, philosophy, anatomy, and kinesiology.

Present physical education texts generally fail to treat in depth relevant generalizations from related disciplines. In these books, one or two physical education authors have attempted to present a series of "principles" of physical education in a few chapters, each of which contains some reference to knowledge in various fields. In today's world of rapidly expanding knowledge, one or two authors can no longer be well versed in several disciplines sufficiently to write principles and foundations books in physical education, which possess the depth and sophistication required to understand and describe the field, and to guide its practices.

With rare exceptions, scholars of other disciplines have not devoted their major attention to investigation and reports which concern physical education phenomena. Thus, for example, the historians have virtually neglected the history of sport in general history books and few sociologists have studied sports as their major line of inquiry.

Nonetheless a vast accumulation of knowledge exists in the literature of the foundation fields which has direct and essential relevance to physical education. Most of this knowledge has not been accumulated systematically or reported and interpreted accurately to the physical education profession. The task of selecting and reporting relevant generalizations from any one discipline requires a physical education scholar who is also a scholar of the related subject.

For the first time in physical education literature, this series incorporates books about physical education, prepared by distinguished physical education scholars, who have established reputations for knowledge and competence in the subject matter and in the principal modes of inquiry in the related fields. Thus, each volume synthesizes recent knowledge into usable form for students and teachers and is unique in physical education literature. Furthermore, the reader is instructed in the process of developing his own *principles* of physical education from his increasing knowledge and understanding. Comprehensive bibliographies list basic references for further study in each field.

This series is appropriate for Foundations or Principles of Physical Education courses at both the undergraduate and graduate levels. Individual volumes are suitable for courses concerning their respective subject areas. Also, these books are valuable for collateral reading and can provide the basis for individual study projects.

The series provides a reference source for the latest knowledge of scientific, behavioral, and humanistic insight and understanding, which constitute the subject and the practice of physical education today. It belongs in the library of every student and teacher of physical education.

J. N.

Preface

Kinesiology, or the science of human motion, is based on a knowledge of the anatomy and physiology of the neuromusculo-skeletal system and the physical laws of force, motion, and gravity. Thus, the author has attempted to present a brief discussion of the functioning of the various segments of the human body and of the most important principles involved in the various types of movement tasks which must be undertaken by man.

This book is intended as an overview which, it is hoped, will raise more questions in the mind of the reader than it answers, and thus motivate him to delve more deeply into the literature and to study more detailed references.

M. B.

Contents

AN
INTRODUCTION
TO
KINESIOLOGY

I

Kinesiology Defined

Kinesiology broadly defined is the study of the science of movement—its anatomical, physiological, mechanical, psychological, and sociological aspects. Frequently in the past, the term was used to indicate only the study of the anatomy of movement. Thus for some time kinesiology was considered to be only applied anatomy, and courses labelled "Kinesiology" encompassed little beyond the study of the muscle action involved in various simple and complex movements. Many of these analyses were greatly simplified and were based on movements theorized from the locations of origins and insertions of muscles and the fact that when a muscle contracts it shortens. They paid little heed to the effects of outside forces which might be involved.

Today it is realized that to understand human movement, one must understand not only the ways in which the body can move or be moved and the laws that govern efficient movement, but also the ways in which the human being is motivated to move and the effects this motion has on the total person— his body (mechanically and physiologically), his emotions, and his concepts concerning himself and his environment.

Since physical education is concerned with movement, with helping people understand their bodies and the way in which they can manipulate them effectively, kinesiology is an important area of study for physical educators. It is important also to others who work in the areas of sports medicine and rehabilitation—the coach, physician, and physical and occupational therapist. Although their emphases differ, all are interested in efficient use of the body.

Most curricula designed for physical education or therapy majors include a course entitled "Kinesiology." Obviously no one course can delve into *all* the facets of human movement and thus any so-called "Kinesiology" course must be limited to certain approaches to the study of the broad area of the science of movement. It cannot embrace all of kinesiology. As currently taught, this course is usually limited to those approaches involving the physical sciences. Wells (3) has indicated that most kinesiology courses are based on biomechanics and musculoskeletal anatomy with some neuromuscular physiology, although the latter is normally dealt with in more detail in a separate course entitled "Physiology of Muscular Activity" or "Physiology of Exercise." Kinesiology has usually been defined as the sciences of anatomy, physiology, and mechanics as applied to the analysis of human voluntary movement. This definition suggests a dynamic integration of the function of bone, muscle, nerve, and related structures in the performance of willed movements or patterns of movements under the influence of internal and external forces.

The majority of kinesiology courses today deal both with the structure of the human body and its mechanisms for movement and with the physical laws of the universe which govern movement and, in the final analysis, determine how the body can and cannot move. Thus many such courses include discussions of the neuromuscular bases for, and the application of the physical laws to, human movement as well as the anatomy of movement. Furthermore the analysis of muscular action no longer rests entirely on theoretical bases. With the recent advances in electronics, increasing numbers of electromyographic studies have clarified muscle function during the performance of a variety of simple movements and a few complex motor skills. A recent study by Broer and Houtz (2) recorded the activity of sixty-eight muscles during the performance of thirteen sport skills. However, the study of muscle function by electromyography is still relatively young, and a great deal more research will be required before muscular action is fully understood.

Movement is indicative of life, a fact well known to the mother in the third trimester of pregnancy, when she welcomes the activity of the baby within the womb. For effective growth and development, the infant and child must progress through a definite series of movements and activities within given periods. Through movement he learns about and adapts to his environment. One of the most obvious means of assuring efficient movement by an adult is to lay the groundwork in the early periods of life. Since the neuromuscular system develops only through function, the sooner effective neuromuscular patterns are developed (after the body has reached the required maturation level), the better coordinated, the more economical and predictable the movements of the adult will be.

Man is confronted with a variety of movement tasks that involve everyday living skills, work skills, and recreation skills. Broer (1) has organized those tasks involving movement of large segments of the body into four main types: supportive tasks, suspension tasks, tasks involving motion of the body and/or objects, and tasks involving the receiving of force. The specific tasks which fall under each of these major types are endless.

The great variety of movement tasks, the number of muscles that must function together to maintain a position or to produce any controlled motion, and the intricacy of the neural mechanism which controls them, make the study of muscle function highly complex. It is complicated further by the ability of the human organism to make use of various muscles at different times to accomplish the same purpose and thus reduce the problem of fatigue.

The human body is unique among objects in the universe in that it has a built-in mechanism with which it can control its position and movements. Nevertheless it, like any other object, is subject to the physical laws of the universe. Therefore, the basic mechanical laws must be understood if human movement is to be understood.

The first section of this book attempts to summarize the general concepts concerning the body's mechanism for movement. To facilitate the study of this section, general concepts of anatomy and reflex patterns are first discussed and then the muscle action is presented from the standpoint of the functions of the various regions of the body. The second section of the book deals with the most important mechanical concepts as they relate to a few selected tasks confronted by man. For clarity the discussion of the mechanical laws has been divided into four sections dealing with their application to tasks which primarily involve support, suspension, movement, and the receipt of force.

REFERENCES

1. Broer, Marion R. *Efficiency of Human Movement*. Philadelphia: W. B. Saunders Company, 1966.
2. Broer, Marion R. and Sara Jane Houtz. *Patterns of Muscular Activity in Selected Sport Skills: An Electromyographic Study*. Springfield: Charles C Thomas, Publisher, 1967.
3. Wells, Katharine F. *Kinesiology*. Philadelphia: W. B. Saunders Company, 1960.

II

Body's Mechanism
for Movement

contributed by
Sara Jane Houtz

SELECTED GENERALIZATIONS
OF ANATOMY

The osseous framework of the body, beautifully designed, affords support and protection for organs and tissues and attachments for muscles, tendons, and ligaments. In addition, bone is a living organ acting as an electrolytic reservoir to assist in maintaining physiological stability. Vital centers located centrally are surrounded by comparatively innumerable compact bones (head, vertebrae, thorax, and pelvis), while the longer bones of the extremities act as levers for support, locomotion, and purposeful activities. The skull and vertebrae encase the central nervous system, teleceptors or distant sensory receptors, and spinal cord. The rib cage attached to the twelve thoracic vertebrae posteriorly and the sternum anteriorly, encases the heart and lungs. The pelvis, besides being the base and protection for organs of the abdominal cavity, is the foundation upon which the spine is balanced. This comparatively rigid ring is in turn set on the heads of the femurs, which with the bones of the legs and feet make up the lower extremities.

Movement is augmented or limited by the shapes of the surfaces joining one bone to another. Periarticulations, with their intervening hyaline cartilage, are constructed for stability and/or ease of movement. Interarticular cartilage or menisci deepen the comparatively flat surface, prevent joint surfaces from coming together, and act as a buffer against longitudinal or rotary forces. The elastic property of cartilage permits changes in shape with changes in joint motion. In some places cartilage is used to connect bony surfaces, as in the case of costal cartilage, which connects the ribs to the sternum.

Synovial articular surfaces may have both gliding and rotary or rocking motion, owing to the inequality of the extent of joint surfaces between the two bones. The curved and incongruous surfaces of the joints are effective in permitting the viscous synovial fluid to act as an elastic property between a fixed and a movable surface. Joint surfaces maintain their continuity by ligamental and fascial structures, by muscle tension, and by atmospheric pressure. Synovial fluid is encased within the synovial membranes surrounding the joint. The inner surface of the fibrous capsule is a closed sac, the synovial cavity, which is lined by the synovial membrane. All freely moving joints are enveloped by such an intra-articular capsule.

Ligaments are composed of strong, tough elastic tissue and, depending on their function, vary somewhat in histological makeup. The bundles of collagenous fibers permit perfect freedom of movement but at the same time are strong enough to resist the stresses and forces applied during dynamic activities. Ligaments have several functions: they attach one bone to another around a joint; they bind two bones together without a joint, thus permitting slight motion; they stretch from one process to another on the same bone, thus restricting structures beneath them. The last mentioned ligaments are most common where numerous tendons cross a joint. Ligaments are strongest and most numerous in areas where the greatest stress occurs. For example, fibrous connective tissue in the sole of the foot is strong and extensive to assist the bony and muscle structures in maintaining the arches of the foot.

The force for moving the bones is supplied by muscles which cross one or more joints. The placement and type of attachment of the muscles on the bone vary with functions. They may have long tendinous origins, as the biceps brachii, or numerous bony and fascial origins, as the gluteus maximus, or as in numerous other cases, the fibers may be attached directly to the bone. Insertions are as varied. Where tendinous attachments occur, muscle contraction must take up the slack in the tendon before it is effective in moving the bone. Muscle tissues have the properties of elasticity, distensibility, and plasticity. Through exercise muscle tissue develops in strength and endurance. When it contracts, a muscle tends to pull origin and insertion points closer together. During contraction, a muscle may shorten (isotonic), remain the same length (isometric), or gradually elongate when a load greater than the maximum contraction tension is applied. This last type has been termed "lengthening contraction" by Fulton (1). The most common types of movement involve isotonic contraction; for example, raising the hand to the mouth, throwing, catching, hitting, or any activity in which a muscle produces movement of the segment. Isometric contraction occurs when the load is so great that there is no movement, or during static support of one part while another segment may be moved.

Contraction occurs as a result of chemical, electrical, and mechanical changes. The development of specialized instruments has permitted the recording of the electrical activity of muscles during the performance of a variety of activities. This has been extremely valuable in giving a better understanding of muscle function. Anatomically, the origin and the insertion of many muscles are so placed that the general pull of the muscle is in a spiral direction. This requires other muscles to assist in the control of a movement. For all functional purposes, isolated contraction of a single muscle is rare. In reality, groups of muscles react from either attachment at a given time or during a definite period to perform the most simple of movements. At a given time, a muscle may serve in part or completely, as a prime mover or as a synergist. Synergistic action may serve to stabilize the neighboring body segment to which one end of the prime mover is attached, or to assist the prime mover in executing the desired movement.

The moving force of the muscles is supplied by the central nervous system through the sensorimotor nerves. Gooddy (3, 4) believed that patterns of sensation rather than patterns of movement are learned. All movement is a sensorimotor experience. Without the afferent (sensory) stimulus, there can be no efferent (motor) response. Proprioceptive sensory organs in the muscles, tendons, and joints transmit to higher neural centers the position of the joint and the degree of effort needed to move an object.

Pressure organs, tactile sensation, and heat and cold receptors in the dermal layers of the skin orient the person to the outside atmosphere. Teleceptors (or distant receptors) in the head, such as the eye, the ear, and the nose, orient the person to his environment by conveying sights, sounds, and odors to the central nervous system. The cerebellum, vestibular mechanisms, eyes, and reflex centers of the neck and midbrain function to adjust the posture of the body in space during static and dynamic movement. Patterns of sensation and resultant patterns of movement are integrated at all levels of the central nervous system. During an activity, a person concentrates on the purpose or objective, while numerous movements made at a subconscious level correctly position the various body parts at a specific time and to the desired degree. Accidentally touching a hot object elicits a simple withdrawal reflex response. Raising a glass to the lips sets up a pattern stimulus in the skin and proprioceptive end organs in the muscles, tendons, and joints so that the glass will not be broken by too much pressure and it will reach the lips without being thrown over the shoulder. More complicated activities such as playing the organ, in which all four extremities have their own patterns of activity, require the functioning not only of the simplest of sensorimotor patterns, but of higher centers of the nervous system. The work of Gellhorn (2) has demonstrated that movements rather than muscles are represented in the motor cortex. He showed that when the cortex was stimulated, the muscles that contracted depended on the angle of the joint. For instance, stimulation of the same cortical area would elicit contraction of the triceps (extensors) when the elbow was at an acute angle and of the biceps when it was at an obtuse angle. Certain muscles are linked together neurologically to perform a movement against resistance. The biceps brachii, wrist and finger flexors, and posterior deltoid act when the forearm is in pronation and supported. Passive resistance to the hip flexors of the seated subject elicits simultaneous contraction of the ankle dorsiflexors, namely, the tibialis anterior. Sherrington (6, 7) has demonstrated that when extension of a joint is desired, a strong flexion contraction preceding the action intensifies the subsequent extensor contraction. Kabat (5) found that strong alternate isometric contractions of the flexors and extensors may be used to facilitate a powerful or forceful isotonic movement. Thus the backswing of the throw, besides contributing to a forceful delivery by giving time and distance for the development of momentum, places the extremity in a position to take advantage of neuromuscular facilitation making possible even greater force. This type of preparation for activity is seen in all sports. The repetitive effort to use these facilitation techniques should improve the pattern of action.

REFERENCES

1. Fulton, J. F. (Editor). *A Textbook of Physiology* (17th Ed.). Philadelphia: W. B. Saunders Company, 1955, chapter 8.
2. Gellhorn, E. *Physiological Foundations of Neurology and Psychiatry.* Minneapolis: Univ. of Minnesota Press, 1953, chapter 3.
3. Gooddy, W. "Sensation and Volition," *Brain,* 72:312 (1949).
4. Gooddy, W. and M. Reinhold. "Some Aspects of Human Orientation in Space," *Brain,* 75:472 (1952); 76:337 (1953).
5. Kabat, H., M. McLeon, M. and C. Holt. "The Practical Application of Proprioceptive Neuromuscular Facilitation," *Physiotherapy,* April 1959.
6. Sherrington, C. *Man on His Nature* (2nd Ed.). Garden City, N.Y.: Doubleday & Company, Inc., 1955.
7. Sherrington, C. *The Integrative Action of the Nervous System* (2nd Ed.). New Haven: Yale University Press, 1947.
8. Steindler, A. *Kinesiology of the Human Body.* Springfield, Ill.: Charles C Thomas, Publisher, 1955.

section two

REFLEX PATTERNS

Assumed postures and voluntary movements are superimposed on a background of attitudinal or postural reactions. These mechanisms are automatic adjustments to changes in position, contactual stimuli, and the force of gravity. The most outstanding investigations of reflex activity of the nervous system emanated from the laboratories of Sherrington (10) and Magnus (4, 5, 6, 7) in approximately the same period. These men studied, by section at various levels of the animal's brain and spinal cord, the location of reflex centers, the interaction of the reflex patterns, and their integration in the nervous system. Sherrington introduced the idea that all normal movement patterns are preceded by reflex patterns.

Recent works of Paine (8), Pieper (9), and others studying the newborn infant, have given insight into human activity with incomplete cerebral maturation. The human infant at birth demonstrates survival reflexes (startle, sucking, swallowing, respiratory) and static positioning reflexes, but cannot perform movements to overcome gravitational forces. Results of extensive studies of the premature and full-term infant, and the baby as he develops in the first years of life, have been comparable in many respects to those obtained in studies done on animals.

In essence, reflexes of position and movement appear at specific points in the development of the cerebral function. They occur early in life and are rapidly brought under the control of higher nervous centers. Increasing importance has been placed on the sequence and timing of these reflexes for normal development. Pathological conditions may be indicated if these reflexes appear out of phase or are not cortically controlled within a definite time period. Pieper demonstrated the stepping reflex pattern, not unlike the normal stride, in a newborn baby when the head and trunk were supported in the erect position. This is apparently not associated with the labyrinthine system, since the infant will progress up the wall and across the ceiling. Space does not permit a detailed discussion of this broad subject. The reader may pursue the subject by further study of the references.

One of the most primitive reflex patterns is the *self-preservation reaction.* This mass reaction takes various forms of withdrawal from the unexpected approach of an object. The stimulus may be visual, auditory, or tactile. Most car drivers have experienced a withdrawal reaction when an unexpected object hits the windshield. The small child, on his first attempt to catch a ball, usually closes his eyes and very often attempts to ward off the object rather than catch it. The line drive of the ball off a bat toward the pitcher may create a withdrawal reaction. Only by suppression of this reflex pattern can an attempt to catch the ball be made. At times, this self-preservation reaction is protective, at other times it must be centrally inhibited.

Postural or attitudinal reflexes are classified according to the anatomical extent of reaction. *Local Static Reactions* are confined to a single segment of the body and include the stretch reflex and the positive supporting reaction. The basic postural reflex is the response of the contractile component of a muscle to its incorporated sensory receptor acting through a segment of the spinal cord. When a muscle is stretched, the sensory organ muscle spindle lying within and parallel to the muscle fibers is also stretched. This stretching excites an impulse which passes over the afferent (sensory) neurons through a synapse with the efferent (motor) neuron to the muscle causing it to contract. The monosynaptic pathway between a motor and a sensory neuron also appears to have synaptic connections which weakly facilitate synergistic muscles. It is now generally believed that an inhibitory neuron is also involved in the pathway which inhibits the antagonist. All skeletal muscles have muscle spindles, although the number varies in different muscles. It is thought that the greatest number of spindles occur in those muscles which oppose gravitational forces. The easiest stretch reflex to demonstrate is the knee jerk. A sharp tap on the patella tendon of the flexed knee stretches the muscle spindle further, causing a contraction of the quadriceps.

The reflex is limited to the muscle stretched. This has functional significance in that it is important in a smooth adjustment to any shift of the center of gravity which changes the muscles under stretch. This reflex is also functional in the coordination of running, walking, and all movements made in the erect posture.

For additional information on the monosynaptic reflex, attention is directed to the following articles:

1. Earl Eldred, M.D., "The Dual Sensory Role of Muscle Spindles," *Physical Therapy Journal,* 45:4 (April 1965).

2. Victor J. Wilson, "Inhibition in the Central Nervous System," *Scientific American,* May 1966.

The positive supporting reaction demonstrates the functional importance of these stretch reflexes. When a child is gently lowered feet first to the floor, there is a tendency for the body weight to flex the extremities, but when the feet strike the floor the extensor spindles in the foot muscles are stretched, and through the stretch reflex, the extensor muscles contract and the limb is transformed into a supporting pillar.

Segmental Static Reactions involve a number of neurons and the synapses of sensory and motor systems from both extremities within a segment of the cord. Painful stimulus to the hand or foot causes a total withdrawal or reflex flexion contraction of the extremity. If the person is in an erect position, a flexion reflex elicited in the one extremity is associated with a contralateral extension. This is commonly known as a *crossed extension reflex.* In other words, as one leg is flexed, the other is extended and the erect posture is thus protected.

General Static Reactions are considered those reflexes which are initiated in one part of the body and influence a number of segments. The *tonic reflexes* are thought to be integrated in the high cervical region. Positioning of the head influences position of the extremities. The asymmetrical tonic neck reflex is a well-known attitudinal reflex because of its uncontrollable persistence in some children with cerebral palsy. Turning the head to one side increases the extensor tonus of the extremity of the chin side and decreases the tonus in the limb on the other side (Fig. 1). This has been described by neurologists as the "fencing stance." The position of the archer with his head turned toward the target takes advantage of this reflex mechanism, since he needs stabilization of the extended extremity to hold the bow while the flexed extremity draws the string (Fig. 1). Photographs of sport activities invariably show the head turned and often tilted toward the active arm as it is extended. This is particularly true under periods of stress. Hellebrandt and co-workers (2) have demonstrated that the position of the head facilitates the work output of the wrist flexors and extensors during exhausting exercises on an ergograph. The influence of rotary movements of the head on the arms may be a hazard when driving an automobile. Unless the arm positions are consciously set as the head is turned, there is a tendency for the hands on the wheel to move in the direction of the turning.

Anteroposterior positioning of the head also influences the tonus in the extremities. Forward flexion of the head, tucking the chin in strongly, increases the extensor tonus of the lower extremities and decreases the tonus of the upper extremities. Tipping the head backward and chin upward decreases the extensor tonus of the lower extremities and increases the tonus of the upper extremities. A cat with a piece of meat held above him will extend the head, flex the hindquarters, and extend the forequarters in a preparatory position to jump. This crouched posture is not unlike that of

FIG. 1.

Asymmetrical tonic neck reflex position of a
supine newborn infant (left) and position of
archer (right).

the football lineman or the sprinter when a powerful drive or quick getaway
is important. Many cats, and some linemen, during the period of waiting for
the drive or jump, will shift their hindquarters from side to side, thus rein-
forcing the reflex and hence the effort.

In an effort to demonstrate tonic neck reflexes, Hellebrandt, *et al.* (3)
presented 103 photographs of five normal individuals during various positions and movements. The effect of movement of the head on the limbs varies
with the position of the body and whether or not the weight of the body
is borne by the feet. The position of the head in relation to the movements
of the arms also varies according to the position of the body. This confirms
previous work by Magnus and others. These reflexes appear to play a
significant role in insuring integration of the behavior of the extremities with
the position of the individual.

The influence of the *neck righting reflex* of the body and the *body righting
reflexes* of the head have been demonstrated in the infant in a supine
position. The first reflex is elicited by turning the head sideward. As the
head is turned, each adjacent section follows until the whole body is prone.
The second reflex is elicited by grasping both legs of the baby and rotating
them on the vertical body axis. As the legs are moved the trunk and head
will follow.

Coordination of the upper and lower extremities during what Sherrington
called a "total movement pattern" is seen in the crawling child's forward

progression. The legs and arms move in opposition. This total pattern of right arm-left leg, left arm-right leg coordination is seen in all activities and is fundamental to balance and locomotion.

Pieper described the chain reflexes in the infant which occur as the *labyrinthine righting reflex* of the head develops. This series of events enables the body to take any position while the head remains upright in space. Initially the baby cannot lift its head from the supporting surface. Gradually, the child in the prone position raises the head so that it is in a normal position in space. The gaze is forward and upward (Fig. 2). This lifting of the head triggers a supporting reaction of the arms which tends to extend them and lift the shoulders off the surface. He moves from side to side or progresses forward with little participation of the lower extremities. Even-

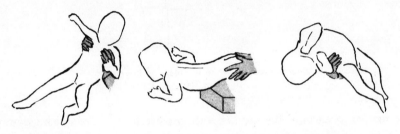

FIG. 2.

Figures on right and left were supported in oblique position; one in center was supported under pelvis with trunk extended over edge of table. Labyrinth righting reflex of 11-month-old infant effectively demonstrated in first and second figures; in newborn (third figure) reflex not developed and baby is unable to orient his head in space.

tually the child flexes the lower extremities, and from this position he attains the crawling posture with the upper extremities extended and lower ones flexed. From then on he will maintain the head in the normal position in space regardless of the posture of the trunk and extremities.

The ability to orient the head and body in relation to the ground during projectile activities such as pole vaulting, diving, gymnastics, and leaps in dancing enable the individual to land feet first, or in the case of diving, head first. The ability to right oneself in space is a composite of a number of *righting reflexes*. The pole vaulter is not unlike the cat which, when supported under the back with the paws in the air will, upon release, turn over and land on all fours. This quick progression is initiated by the head with the forefeet, trunk, and hind legs following.

The *labyrinthine accelerating reflexes* associated with the labyrinth or vestibular organ are extremely important in movement. The primary function of the vestibular organ is to respond to acceleration or deceleration in speed of movement. The sensory stimuli, initiated by changes in the semi-circular canals in the inner ear, are particularly important in adjusting to rotary movements of the body. Whenever the head is rotated for any period of time, either by rolling or twisting, the fluid in the inner ear is put into motion. Because an object in motion tends to remain in motion (inertia), this movement of the fluid in the inner ear continues even after the motion of the head has stopped. When reflex adjustments are made to this false sense of motion, balance is upset. This effect can be minimized if the head is turned rapidly and held momentarily with the eyes focused on a point (*see* optic reflex (below) before the next turn, a technique often employed by dancers.

If a nine- or ten-month-old infant supported on the hands in a prone position is moved through space, the back arches and the upper and lower extremities tend to extend and abduct. This reflex position in response to acceleration was first described by Magnus and is presently known as the *Landau reflex*. A refinement of this reflex mechanism may be seen momentarily in the swan dive before the diver adjusts his position for entry into the water.

In addition to the vestibular mechanism, the *optical reflexes* are most important in gaining or maintaining control of the body in space. Their importance can be demonstrated easily by standing on one foot first with the eyes open and then closed. While balance can be maintained even over this small base when the eyes are open, it is almost impossible when they are closed. In addition, there is a very close association between eye and neck movements. In movements of the head the eyes adjust to maintain the center of focus. The above-mentioned technique of turning the head rapidly and focusing on a point momentarily when twirling also involves the optic reflexes.

Locomotor activities are comprised of reactions previously introduced as reflexes. They are actions compounded of posture and movement. The postural component maintains the erect position and momentarily balances the weight on one extremity as the body moves forward. The dynamic component involves the rhythmic alternating movement of the limbs.

Much of this discussion has been concerned with the reactions to external stimuli or position change. Throughout the process of development an innate "spark," apparently in response to internal stimulus, controls and integrates at all levels of the central nervous system, the more primitive movement patterns.

REFERENCES

1. Fulton, J. F. (Editor). *A Textbook of Physiology* (17th Ed.). Philadelphia: W. B. Saunders Company, 1955.
2. Hellebrandt, F. A., S. J. Houtz, M. J. Partridge and C. E. Walters. "Tonic Neck Reflexes in Exercises of Stress in Man," *Amer. J. Phys. Med.,* 35:144 (June 1956).
3. Hellebrandt, F. A., M. Schade and M. L. Carns. "Methods of Evoking the Tonic Neck Reflexes in Normal Human Subjects," *Amer. J. Phys. Med.,* 41:90 (1962).
4. Magnus, R. and A. deKleijn. "Experimental Physiology of the Labyrinth," *Proc. Roy. Soc. Med., Sec. Otol.,* 17:6 (1924).
5. Magnus, R. *Körperstellung.* Berlin: Julius Springer, 1924.
6. Magnus, R. "On the Cooperation and Interference of Reflexes from Other Sense Organs with Those of the Labyrinths," *Laryngoscope,* 36:701 (1926).
7. Magnus, R. "Some Results of Studies in the Physiology of Posture," *Lancet,* 104:531 (Sept. 11, 1926); *ibid.,* 104:585 (Sept. 18, 1926).
8. Paine, R. S., T. B. Brazelton, D. E. Donovan, J. E. Drorbaugh, J. P. Hubbell and E. M. Sears. "Evolution of Postural Reflexes in Normal Infants and in the Presence of Chronic Brain Syndromes," *Neurology,* 14:1036 (1964).
9. Pieper, A. *Cerebral Function in Infancy and Childhood* (Trans. 3rd revised German Ed. by B. and H. Nagler). N.Y.: Consultants Bureau, 1963, chapters 4–5.
10. Sherrington, C. *The Integrative Action of the Nervous System* (2nd Ed.). New Haven: Yale University Press, 1947.
11. Waterland, J. C. and F. A. Hellebrandt. "Involuntary Patterning Associated with Willed Movement Performed Against Progressively Increasing Resistance," *Amer. J. Phys. Med.,* 43:13 (1964).

PELVIS AND LOWER EXTREMITIES

The pelvic ring, unlike the mobile shoulder girdle, is rigid with relatively no movement between the articular surfaces. It consists of the three bones on either side (ilium, pubis, and ischium) and the sacrum posteriorly. The hip joints placed laterally are ball-and-socket in type and permit motion between the pelvis and lower extremities. Flexion, abduction, adduction, and rotation can be performed through a comparatively wide range of motion, while extension beyond that achieved in the erect posture is limited by the joint structure and the ilio-femoral, ischio-femoral, and pubo-femoral ligaments.

The reported degrees of hip extension beyond the position assumed in the erect posture have varied from slightly under 180 degrees of extension to as much as 30 to 45 degrees of retroposition or hyperextension. As yet there is no unanimous agreement among investigators as to the line of reference of the pelvis which should be used for comparison with the anatomical axis of the femur. As a result there is this variability in range of hyperextension of the thigh. Another movement sometimes overlooked occurs between the lumbar spine and sacrum and is actually hyperextension of the back.

Flexion and extension of the knee are the combined action of a gliding and rocking motion between the femur and tibia. Since the line of gravity in the erect posture falls in front of the center of the knee, gravity favors extension of the knee. The articular structure requires an "easy" position of the knees in the erect posture, since maximum extension places undue pressure on the joint structures.

Dorsiflexion and plantar flexion occur at the ankle articulation of the tibia-fibula and talus bones. Other motions, foot inversion (supination and adduction) and eversion (pronation and abduction), occur in the tarsal joints, primarily the talocalcaneonavicular articulation. The structure of the

17

foot is designed primarily for support and locomotion. Thus, movement and flexibility of the foot as compared to the hand are limited. The curved surfaces of the tarsal and metatarsal bones, each fitting snugly at the articulation with the adjacent bones, form a resilient and elastic longitudinal arch. As in the hand, the medial and lateral borders of the feet have distinct form, structure, and function. The lateral borders with the heels and the balls of the feet support the body weight during standing. The medial surface is dome-shaped to form a strong, dynamic arch which participates during activities of propulsion. During the stance phase of walking, the weight-bearing area of the foot advances from the heel over the lateral surface of the foot to the ball and across it, hence to the toes as they grip the ground as the foot pushes off. After the swing phase, the heel contacts the ground and, as the body weight is shifted forward, the same pattern of weight bearing occurs. Sprinting, or activities in which the body weight is maintained on the balls and toes of the feet, requires the toe flexor muscles to grip the surface as the extrinsic "sling" muscles, peroneus longus, and tibialis anterior and posterior, project or thrust the body forward. Equally important is the ability of the foot to absorb the force of impact and maintain balance on this comparatively small surface as it contacts the ground in the stride phase.

In the lower extremity, muscle fibers interdigitate with the sheaths covering them to add strength and power. Muscles are divided by silvery, shiny connective tissue which permits one muscle to glide across another with little or no friction. While the muscle attachments of the upper extremity and hand are discrete and localized, those of the lower extremity and foot are broad and widespread to allow greater power and versatility in the weight-bearing position.

The pelvis offers attachment for the abdominal and back muscles and the thigh and leg muscles. Strong fascial sheaths and ligaments bind the femurs to the pelvis and to the lumbar spine. For instance, the gluteus maximus, in addition to its attachment to the bone, arises from the aponeurosis of the sacrospinalis muscle, the sacral tuberous ligament, and the fascia gluteal aponeurosis covering the deeper muscles. The fibers are directed obliquely downward and laterally to insert into, both the bony attachment of the gluteal tuberosity and the ilio-tibial band of the fascia lata, of which the small tensor fascia lata muscle has major attachment. This strong aponeurosis runs the entire length of the thigh to attach to the leg below the knee.

The iliopsoas is unique in that these two deep muscles have a common tendinous insertion on the femur, although some fibers from the iliacus also insert several inches below this. The long, narrow psoas, lying anteriorly to the lumbar spine, originates from these processes and the twelfth rib. The broad, flat iliacus lying inside the ilium originates from its crest. The function of the iliopsoas is to flex the thigh on the pelvis or the pelvis on the thigh. The anatomical difference between the psoas and the iliacus suggests that they have other separate functions. Six small deep muscles and the gluteus medius and minimus muscles, originating on the pelvis and inserting on the femur, contribute to the action of the thigh. The medially placed adductor group function not only as thigh adductors but also contribute to other movements depending on whether the thigh is flexed or extended.

One head of the quadriceps muscle (the rectus femoris) and three portions of the hamstring muscle (the semimembranosis, semitendonosis, and the long head of the biceps) insert on the pelvis; the other portions have attachments on the femur. Tendons of the four portions of the quadriceps unite to incorporate the patella and insert on the tibial tubercle. Two heads of the hamstring muscle insert on the medial condyles of the tibia, while the long and short heads insert on the lateral aspect of the leg. Diarticular muscles contribute to motion at both joints. The position of one joint influences the length of these muscles and may restrict or enhance movement at the adjacent joint.

All extrinsic muscles acting on the foot except the gastrocnemius originate from the tibia and fibula. This muscle arises from two attachments above the two condyles of the femur. Prior to birth, however, the gastrocnemius muscle originates below the epiphyseal line. As the infant learns to crawl, toddle, and walk this muscle migrates upward on the shaft of the femur finally to attain the attachment seen in adults at surgery or as illustrated in the standard anatomy books. The attachment on the femur and the increased angle of application of pull as it passes over the condyles of the femur suggest the functional importance of the gastrocnemius at the knee. Anatomically, the tendon of Achilles is derived mainly from the soleus muscle and is joined by muscle fibers and the deep tendon of the gastrocnemius at midleg. The attachment of the Achilles tendon on the posterior aspect of the calcaneus offers resistance to all extrinsic muscles attached to the tarsal, metatarsal, and phalangeal bones, the small intrinsic muscles, and the taut plantar fascia. With the possible exceptions of the tibialis anterior and the flexor digitorum longus, the other extrinsic muscles arise mainly from the fibula and interosseous membrane. The tibialis anterior has its origin primarily on the anterior portion of the tibia, while the flexor digitorum longus arises mainly from the posterior portion of the tibia. The long toe flexors and posterior tibialis muscles traverse from the posterior aspect of the fibula across the back of the leg, losing the fleshy fibers to tendons, which ultimately pass behind the tibial malleolus and hence to plantar attachments on the foot. The angular direction of many of the extrinsic muscles and the devious routes of their tendons behind the malleoli, around the border and under the foot, act through pulley systems to increase the leverage action and thus the force and power important to the function of the foot. In addition to the extrinsic muscles and the bony construction of the feet, the strong intrinsic muscles, fascial sheaths, and widespread aponeuroses assist in the support of the arches.

The posture of the superimposed parts as they influence the adjustment of the body's center of gravity during a specific activity must be understood and taken into account when analyzing the muscle function of the supportive appendages. In the weight-bearing postures, muscles function from their attachment on the foot or leg to adjust the leg, thigh, and pelvis over the base. Recent electromyographic studies have been extremely helpful in clarifying the function of lower extremity muscles in the weight-bearing posture.

Figure 3 illustrates the patterns of electrical activity in the muscles of the thigh and leg as influenced by a shift in the center of gravity. During forward flexion of the trunk with the knees extended (1), the hamstring muscle, and to a lesser degree the triceps surae and tibialis anterior, were active. As the subject flexed the knees in this position, these muscles continued to act (upper illustration 2) with slightly increased electrical activity occurring in the quadriceps muscle. As the subject continued to flex the knees (lower record 2), the action was performed almost entirely by the quadriceps muscle to resist forces tending to flex the knees. During extension of the knees (3), the hamstring, triceps surae, and tibialis anterior muscles were again active. The hamstring and, to a lesser degree, the triceps surae muscles remained active until, with a burst of activity in the tibialis anterior, the erect posture was assumed (4). Patterns of electrical activity recorded from the supporting extremity (numbered electromyograms) and from the contralateral extremity (outline drawings superimposed on records) during simple movements are illustrated in Figure 4. The hamstring muscle functions as a knee flexor during the activity as performed in the upper right corner; in all other activities illustrated, it acts either as a hip extensor or to resist hip flexion. Thus, which muscles of the thigh and leg participate in a prescribed activity, and their specific functions, are influenced by the position of various body segments.

Anatomical textbooks state that the gluteus maximus muscle is a strong thigh extensor; however, electromyographic studies have shown it to be active primarily in the very small range of terminal hip extension or hyperextension. The greatest magnitude of electrical activity in this muscle is elicited during strong volitional contraction (muscle setting) with the thigh in the extended position.

Studies indicate that although some thigh muscles may be active in maintaining a relaxed standing position, their action is not necessary. The primary muscles responsible for maintaining this posture are the gastrocnemius and soleus. Analyses of their functions indicate that the former acts at the knee and the latter at the ankle. During locomotion, the gastrocnemius and soleus are active during the stance phase (as the contralateral extremity is in the swing phase), while the tibialis anterior acts to pull the leg over the foot at the end of the supportive phase and continues to act until the heel is placed on the ground.

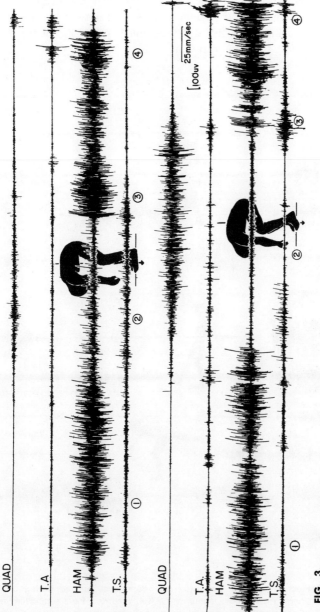

FIG. 3.

Effect of shifting center of gravity on patterns of muscle action. Sequence of actions: (1) trunk forward flexion, (2) knee flexion, (3) knee extension, (4) movement to an erect posture. Knees flexed to approximately 20 degrees in upper electromyogram and 90 degrees in lower record. Symbols: Quad., Quadriceps; T.A., Tibialis Anterior; Ham., Hamstrings; T.S., Triceps Surrae. (Courtesy Journal Applied Physiology, 10:999, 1964.)

Neuromuscular control of muscles of the lower extremities in the weight-bearing position is usually at a subconscious level. Changes in postures of the trunk, shoulder girdle, and upper extremities elicit contraction in selected muscle groups to maintain the center of gravity over the base of support and thus preserve balance. The focus of attention is primarily on the movement being performed by the upper extremity.

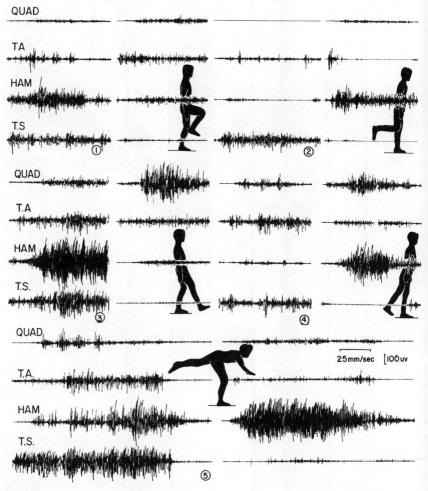

FIG. 4.

Comparison of action potential patterns from one subject, elicited during a variety of activities. Electromyograms above numbers 1,2,3,4, recorded from supporting extremity; first four figure drawings superimposed on records from moving extremity. For lowest maneuver (5) electromyograms to left indicate support and to right, moving extremity. Symbols: Quad., Quadriceps; T.A., Tibialis Anterior; Ham., Hamstrings; T.S., Triceps Surrae. (Courtesy *Journal Applied Physiology,* 19:999, 1964.)

REFERENCES

1. Basmajian, J. V. *Muscles Alive, Their Function Revealed by Electromyography.* Baltimore: The Williams & Wilkins Co., 1962.
2. Close, J. R. *Motor Function in the Lower Extremity, Analyses by Electronic Instrumentation.* Springfield: Charles C Thomas, Publisher, 1964, chapters 3, 5.
3. Fischer, F. J. and S. J. Houtz. "Function of the Gluteus Maximus Muscle: An Electromyographic Study." In press.
4. Hagbarth, K. E. "Spinal Withdrawal Reflexes in the Human Lower Limbs," *J. Neurol., Neurosurg. and Psychiat.,* 23:222 (1960).
5. Houtz, S. J. and F. J. Fischer. "An Analysis of Muscle Action and Joint Excursion During Exercise on a Stationary Bicycle," *J. Bone & Joint Surg.,* 41:123 (1959).
6. Houtz, S. J. and F. J. Fischer. "Function of Leg Muscles Acting on Foot as Modified by Body Movements," *J. Appl. Physiol.,* 16:597 (1961).
7. Houtz, S. J., M. J. Lebow and F. R. Beyer. "The Influence of Posture on the Strength of the Knee Flexor and Extensor Muscles," *J. Appl. Physiol.,* 11:475 (1957).
8. Houtz, S. J. and F. P. Walsh. "Electromyographic Analysis of the Function of the Muscles Acting on the Ankle During Weight Bearing with Special Reference to the Triceps Surae," *J. Bone & Joint Surg.,* 41:1469 (1959).
9. Houtz, S. J. "Influence of Gravitational Forces on Function of Lower Extremity Muscles," *J. Appl. Physiol.,* 19:999 (1964).
10. Jones, F. W. *Structure and Function as Seen in the Foot* (2nd Ed.). London: Bailliere, Tindall & Cox, Ltd., 1949.
11. Jonsson, B. and B. Steen. "Function of the Hip and Thigh Muscles in Romburg's Test and 'Standing at Ease.' An Electromyographic Study," *Acta morphol. Neerl-Scand.,* 5:271 (1963).
12. Joseph, J. *Man's Posture Electromyographic Studies.* Springfield: Charles C Thomas, Publisher, 1960.
13. Karlsson, E. and B. Jonsson. "Function of the Gluteus Maximus Muscle, An Electromyographic Study," *Acta morphol. Neerl-Scand.,* 6:161 (1965).
14. Kugelberg, E., K. Edlund and L. Grimby. "An Electromyographic Study of the Nociceptive Reflexes of the Lower Limb. Mechanism of the Plantar Responses," *Brain,* 83:394 (1960).
15. O'Connell, A. L. "Electromyographic Study of Certain Leg Muscles During Movements of the Free Foot and During Standing," *Am. J. Phys. Med.,* 37:289 (1958).
16. Portnoy, H. and F. Morin. "Electromyographic Study of Postural Muscles in Various Positions and Movements," *Am. J. Physiol.,* 186:122 (1956).
17. Slocum, D. B. "Overuse Syndromes of the Lower Leg and Foot in Athletes," *Instructional Course Lectures, Am. Acad. Ortho. Surg.,* 17:359 (1960).

SHOULDER GIRDLE
AND UPPER EXTREMITIES

The anatomical design of the clavicle, scapula, and humerus is an architectural feat permitting maximal function and range of motion of the shoulder girdle and arm. Through the sternoclavicular joint, the curved clavicle placed anteriorly makes the only real connection of this complex to the rest of the body. It acts as a strut to hold the shoulder away from the body so that the arm can function freely, and by rotation on its longitudinal axis contributes 50 to 60 degrees of upper extremity elevation. The lateral end of the clavicle unites with the acromion process, an extension of the spine of the triangular shaped scapula, to form the acromioclavicular joint. The broad acromion process protects the glenohumeral joint against blows from above or from the rear. The coracoid process projecting anteriorly from the neck of the scapula, inferior to the clavicle and medial to the glenoid fossa, is an extremely important binding post for those strong ligaments which connect these two bones together and at the same time allows freedom for limited movement. This projection also affords attachment for the pectoralis minor, short head of the biceps, and coracobrachialis muscles.

Synchronous movements between the clavicle and sternum, the scapula and clavicle, and the humerus and scapula occur during activities of the upper extremity. In addition, movement also occurs between the scapula and thoracic cage. This multiple joint activity favors extensive mobility and places the responsibility of stabilization on muscles and ligaments. Movement of the humerus in the anteroposterior or transverse planes is accompanied by coordinated movement in all of these joints. The humerus has a rotary or pivotal component associated with flexion, extension, and abduction. This is best demonstrated by the following movement. With the arm extended at the side and the thumb pointed in the same direction as the face, forward flex the humerus to shoulder level. The thumb is now pointing upward. Maintaining the thumb in the same position, abduct the extended arm at the same height to the same plane as the body. Return the arm to the side. The thumb is now pointing away from the body. Thus, the humerus has pivoted approximately 90 degrees from the original starting position. Repeat this maneuver, except start with the thumb in the final position. It will be found that the approximate limits of longitudinal rotation of the humerus have now been reached. This pivotal action of the humerus increases the functional use of the hand and arm in many sport activities and adds smoothness to the performance.

The unique single attachment of the shoulder girdle and upper extremities to the rest of the body requires that muscles function to support the part and maintain the scapula close to the trunk as well as contribute to the movement. Fifteen muscles attach to the scapula. Six of these muscles act to rotate, elevate, depress, and support the scapula. The remaining nine muscles are involved in glenohumeral movements. The tendons of four of these muscles lying deep to the deltoid, insert in radial positions on the proximal humerus to form the rotator cuff. They act as a unit to assist the deltoid in movements of flexion, abduction, and extension and contribute to the rotary action of the humerus.

Many of the muscles of the shoulder girdle resemble the shape of a Japanese fan (trapezius, deltoid, latissimus dorsi, pectoralis major, and others) with the fibers converging toward or on the head of the humerus. Other muscles such as the serratus anterior converge on a portion of the scapula. The broad origin permits a versatility of function within a muscle and requires a high degree of coordination. In some instances, a portion of a muscle may act antagonistic to another portion, as occurs in the deltoid. During anteroposterior movements the posterior portion of the deltoid is an extensor of the arm and the anterior portion is a flexor, but both function as a unit with the middle portion when abduction is performed. The importance of stabilization is seen in the function of the shoulder girdle elevators. In order that these muscles may function effectively, other muscles must stabilize the points of origin, namely, the head and cervical spine.

Two or more muscles may contribute to a single movement, but each muscle has an isolated action not performed by the others. This is seen in the interaction of the anterior deltoid and pectoralis muscles. Both may contribute to adduction of the extremity from an abducted position at shoulder height to a forward flexed position parallel to the body. Additional adduction across the chest (touching the elbows) elicits a stronger contraction in the pectoralis major muscles. Direct forward flexion of the extremity elicits strong contraction in the anterior deltoid and biceps brachii muscles. Again the biceps also contributes to movements at the elbow.

Kamon (8) studied the patterns of electrical activity of the upper extremity, shoulder girdle, and trunk muscles of gymnasts during exercises in the arm-supported position on a pommeled horse. Interestingly enough, his results indicate that the shoulder girdle and upper extremity muscles function to support the body during movements of the pelvis and lower extremities.

Photographic and electromyographic analyses of unilateral activities of the shoulder and upper extremity have shown that the "inactive" extremity demonstrates a reciprocal pattern. As one extremity is forward flexed at the shoulder and extended at the elbow, the contralateral one is retracted and flexed. This reciprocal pattern contributes to efficiency of movement, greater stability, and total body coordination. The shoulder girdle with the two long lever arms acting in opposite directions, may contribute to rotary movements of the trunk. They also balance the opposite rotation of the pelvic girdle. These factors in turn require a braking action of selected muscles during forceful movements.

Movement of the elbow is limited to flexion and extension for purposes of strength and for placing the hand in a useful position in relation to the body and to external objects. Both the radius and ulna have surfaces which articulate with the humerus and wrist. Longitudinal rotation in the proximal and distal radioulnar joints permits additional positioning of the hand for finely coordinated movements. During supination-pronation activities, the ulna describes an arc from side to side in the plane posterior to the radius while the radius rotates in the opposite direction.

A comparison of the arm and leg shows that the ulna bone plays a more active part in movements of the forearm, while the fibula adds strength to the leg. During flexion of the humerus, gravity favors extension at the elbow, while during flexion of the thigh, gravity produces flexion at the knee. Likewise during retraction of the humerus, gravity flexes the elbow. The triceps retracts the humerus and extends the elbow while the hamstring muscles extend the thigh and flex the knee. The biceps flexes the arm and assists with flexion of the elbow, while the quadriceps flexes the thigh and extends the knee. The anatomical differences in the upper and lower appendages emphasize the functional differences, namely, that one is used for purposive skilled movements, the other for support and locomotion.

The keystone of hand function is mobility of the wrist; all ranges of motion are possible. Flexion of the wrist is associated with some ulnar deviation, while extension is associated with some radial deviation. Ulnar deviation is most easily accomplished in some flexion, while radial deviation occurs with extension. Movements are performed mainly by the six forearm muscles, whose tendons cross the wrist to insert at the base of the metacarpal bones.

Superficial wrist and long finger flexor and extensor muscles have their origin on the condyles of the humerus and thus they assist in elbow flexion as well as produce movement at the wrist and fingers. Other deep extrinsic muscles originate on the radius and/or ulnar bones. The carpal bones have relatively few muscle attachments; thus they demonstrate free mobility in all directions. The tendons of the extrinsic muscles traverse many joints, thus both flexors and extensors are active, either stabilizing or moving selected joints. Tendons of the long extensor muscles limit finger flexion when the wrist is flexed to a maximum degree. Likewise, the flexors have a limiting function on finger extensors when the wrist is in extreme extension. Power of the fingers is greatest when the wrist is in a neutral or slightly extended position, while the wrist function is greatest when the fingers are midway between flexion and extension.

The pisiform bone has one articulation to the palmar surface of the triangular bone and gives attachment to the flexor carpi ulnaris and abductor digiti quinti muscles. It is the only carpal bone which receives an extrinsic muscle insertion. In this way it probably contributes to the support of the ulnar side of the hand for holding objects in the power grip.

The functional position of the hand is with the wrist in neutral to slight extension, the fingers slightly flexed and the thumb in a line with the radius. This position is also seen in the hand in repose. Three arches of the hand, a longitudinal and two transverse, lend strength for pinching and grasping. The hand has very fine motor and sensory qualities. It also has both dynamic and static functions. It can play the most complicated musical instrument. The fingertips can convey vibration to the deaf ear and read Braille to the blind. It can be used in non-prehensile activities, such as passively carrying an object by a strap (*e.g.*, a suitcase), or pushing or pulling the body or an object into position.

The hand has many prehensile activities; in general, these use variations of two basic positions, power-grip and a precision grasping. When power is required, the thumb is a buttress against the object grasped by the fingers. The position of the thumb in relation to the shaft depends on the size of the object and its use. In some instances it may lie parallel to the shaft; then again it may encircle the handle with the fingers. The hand, in relation to the wrist, is in some ulnar deviation. This grip is exemplified by the hand position for gripping a club, bat, or racket. Precision movements involve the pinching action of the fingers and the object is held by the distal pads of the fingers. The size of the object determines the position of the fingers and the number of fingers used. When a softball is held, the fingers radiate outwardly from the hand and all fingers are required to grip the ball. If the object is the size of a ping pong ball, it may be held in two or possibly three fingers and the thumb. A small object such as a pencil is held and manipulated by the radial side of the hand; the thumb, index, and middle finger perform the skilled precise movement, while the ulnar side of the hand with the little and ring fingers is used mainly for support. A screwdriver is held extended from the center of the palm and gripped by the ulnar side with the middle and index finger and thumb forming a "tripod" to guide the direction of the instrument. If both precision and power (or static support) are required in unilateral activities, the division of function within the hand varies depending on the size of the object. In holding a fencing foil, where both power and precision are important, the fingers lie along the inner curve of the handle and the thumb is adducted and parallel to the handle of the foil. Thus, controlled directions can be given to all movements with ease. The purpose of the activity and the implement used determine the way the hand is used.

The extensor muscles of the wrist contract forcefully to stabilize the wrist in extension during many finger movements. The radial extensor has been shown to function more strongly than the ulnar extensor. During wrist flexion the flexor carpi ulnaris contracts more strongly than the radial flexor.

Seven or eight muscles, depending upon the finger, function to control each digit, and ten muscles are active to perform coordinated movements of the thumb. The lumbrical and interosseous muscles act in coordination with the extrinsic muscles to flex and extend the interphalangeal joints. Loss of function of these muscles would prevent the hand from being placed in a position to catch or grasp a ball.

In some two handed activities, the nondominant hand is often used in an assistive capacity while the dominant hand controls the movement. In single handed activities the nondominant hand is not directly involved. However, the more skill and the greater strength needed in the dominant hand, the more reinforcement occurs in the muscles of the nondominant extremity. In essence, the two upper extremities must be considered partners in any gross motor activity.

For the hand to function effectively, muscles of the shoulder girdle, arm, and trunk must be active to stabilize and assist in placing the upper extremity in the proper position. Muscles may stabilize one bone against another by a longitudinal pull. More commonly, a group of muscles may fix the proximal parts of the extremity in a position so that the distal portion, the hand, can perform the desired activity effectively.

REFERENCES

1. Beevor, C. *The Croonian Lectures on Muscular Movements,* reprinted from *Brit. Med. J.,* p. 881, 1909. New York: The Macmillan Company.
2. Broer, M. R. and S. J. Houtz. *Patterns of Muscular Activity in Selected Sport Skills.* Springfield: Charles C Thomas, Publisher, 1967.
3. Bunnell, Sterling. *Surgery of the Hand* (3rd Ed.). Philadelphia: J. B. Lippincott Co., 1956, chapter 2.
4. Capener, Norman. "The Hand in Surgery," *J. Bone and Joint Surg.,* 38-B: 128 (1956).

5. Codman, E. A. *The Shoulder*. Boston: Thomas Todd, 1934, chapters 1, 2.

6. Dempster, W. T. "Mechanisms of Shoulder Movement," *Arch. Phys. Med. & Rehab.*, 46:49 (1965).

7. Flatt, A. "Kinesiology of the Hand," *Instructional Course Lectures, Amer. Acad. Ortho. Surg.*, pp. 266–81, 1961.

8. Kamon, E. "Electromyography of Static and Dynamic Postures of the Body Supported on the Arms," *J. Appl. Physiol.*, 21:1611 (1966).

9. Long, C. and M. E. Brown. "Electromyographic Kinesiology of the Hand: Muscles Moving the Long Finger," *J. Bone and Joint Surg.*, 46-A:1683 (1964).

10. Lucas, D. B. and V. T. Inman. *Functional Anatomy of the Shoulder Joint*. Univ. of California Med. School, April 1963.

11. Napier, J. R. "The Prehensile Movements of the Human Hand," *J. Bone and Joint Surg.*, 38-B:902 (1956).

HEAD, NECK, AND TRUNK

The human body has a central axis with more or less symmetrical musculo-skeletal structures on either side. The spine is a flexible rod to support and maintain the upright position. It consists of seven cervical, twelve thoracic, five lumbar vertebrae, a sacrum, and a coccyx. The sacrum and coccyx bones are usually considered part of the pelvic ring. The curves of the cervical, dorsal, lumbar, and sacral regions develop during infancy. Multiple joints reinforced by strong ligamentous structures contribute to stability, mobility, and ease of adjustment (Fig. 5).

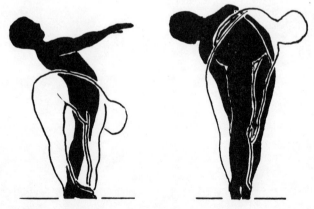

FIG. 5.

Extension of lumbar spine greater than flexion. To resist gravity, abdominal muscles are active during spinal extension and back muscles during flexion. Note degree of hip and lower extremity movement associated with trunk movement.

The bony skull is made up of the cranium (a thick vault to protect and support the brain and membranes) and the bones of the face. The 14 exotically shaped bones of the face lodge sinus cavities, the respiratory passage, and the olfactory, vestibular, auditory, and visual organs. Some special sensory organs are paired (eye, ear), while others are structures formed by symmetrical halves (nose, mouth, and tongue). The mandibular articulation is the only movable joint in the skull. It is a combined hinge and gliding joint which articulates with the temporal bone to perform mastication and vocalization.

The head is balanced on the lateral articulations of the first vertebra— the atlas. The odontoid process of the second vertebral body (axis) projects upward anteriorly through the central opening of the atlas to form the pivotal or rotary articulation with the anterior arch. A thick, strong transverse ligament spans the opening of the atlas to maintain the odontoid process in contact with the anterior arch and separate the bony projection from the spinal cord and its membranes. Thus rotation, flexion, and extension occur between the head and first two cervical vertebrae.

The shapes and articulations of the vertebrae vary from region to region. The greatest ranges of motion in flexion, extension, rotation, and lateral deviation occur in the cervical region. The shape and articulations of the thoracic vertebrae are different from those occurring in the cervical region, thus movement in this area of the spine is limited. The primary movements in the thoracic area are forward flexion and rotation. In the lumbar region, motion is limited primarily to extension and lateral bending. The apparent marked degree of forward flexion of the trunk occurs in the hip articulations rather than in the lumbar region.

All twelve ribs articulate posteriorly with the vertebrae through the costo-vertebral articulation. Anteriorly the first ten ribs articulate with the sternum, the anterior borders of the eleventh and twelfth ribs being free. Extensive cartilage is interposed between the sternum and the eighth, ninth, and tenth ribs. This permits respiratory movements during changes in the volume capacity of the thorax. The vertebral column is relatively rigid, thus movements of the ribs are transmitted to the sternum causing slight movement during respiration. The abdominal cavity is influenced by movement of the diaphragm and thus plays a part in respiratory movements. The bony rib cage protects the contents of the thorax, namely, the heart and lungs and vital blood vessels.

The muscles of the head may be divided into those concerned with the special sense organs such as the eye and ear, those concerned with mastication of food and swallowing, and those concerned with facial expression. Facial expressions reflect the degree of tension during periods of difficult endeavor and severe competition.

Muscles of the neck or suboccipital region may be grouped according to their function. In addition to the extensor muscles of the spine, there are those which function for respiration, swallowing, and vocalization. Still others attach from the head to the cervical spine to produce head movement. Finally, muscles which attach from the head and cervical spine to the shoulder girdle move the head and assist in shoulder girdle movement. When shoulder girdle movement is the primary action, other muscles must stabilize the head to maintain it in a fixed position.

Muscles of the thoracic region contribute to movements of the shoulder girdle and upper extremity. The diaphragm and intercostal muscles are the primary respiratory muscles of the thorax. The diaphragm and abdominal muscles are active during abdominal breathing. Auxiliary respiratory muscles of the suboccipital region and the thoracohumeral and scapulothoracic groups are brought into activity during periods of severe effort. For these muscles to aid in respiration, the head, arms, and shoulder girdle must be stabilized by other muscles.

Extensor muscles of the spine may be grouped as deep, intermediate, or superficial. The deep muscles are relatively short and attach from one segment to another segment to function both as extensors and rotators of the spinal vertebrae. As the extensor muscles become more superficial, they are larger and attach from one segment over several vertebrae. Those which attach more laterally are rotators, while those which attach medially function as extensors. In the erect posture, the extensor muscles contract during forward flexion to resist the force of gravity and permit a smooth movement. Those in the lumbar region are active to stabilize the pelvis during thigh extension and abduction.

Muscles which flex the trunk against gravity and stabilize the pelvis during thigh flexion are the rectus abdominis, obliquus externus and internus, and transversus. The sheath covering the rectus abdominis is formed by the aponeurosis of the obliquus externus, obliquus internus, and transversus muscles from either side. Thus, an important function of the rectus abdominis muscle is to maintain a taut anterior abdominal wall from which the other muscles may contract. Unilateral action of these muscles contributes to lateral flexion and rotation of the spine.

The opening posterior to the bodies of the vertebrae form the housing for the spinal cord and its coverings. Nerves emerging from the anterior portion of the spinal cord have their cells in the gray matter of the anterior horn and are motor nerves to the muscles. Incoming sensory nerves from the periphery have their cells outside the spinal cord and their fibers pass via the posterior root into the spinal cord to synapse with other nerves. Bilateral nerve plexes in the cervical and upper dorsal region supply the muscles of the shoulder girdle and upper extremity. In the lumbar and sacral region, nerves of the bilateral lumbar plexes supply the pelvis and lower extremity muscles.

The simplest movement is a combined adjustment of each body segment starting from a given posture and moving to a new position. The relationship of the head to the trunk, the shoulder girdle to the trunk, the trunk to the pelvis, and the total body to the feet, the supporting base, is important in any movement. The posture in motion has been described by Howorth (6) as the "dynamic" position. For maximum efficiency in the "ready position," the body is in a slightly crouched position with the feet hip-width apart, the weight forward, the hips and knees somewhat flexed, and the ankles dorsiflexed. In this position, gravity and inertia can be overcome and momentum developed with the simplest effort. The force can be directed upward—left, right, or forward. Neurologically, the extensor muscles are put on a stretch and thus they facilitate the extension action required to create the forward thrust of the following movement. This is in keeping with what Sherrington calls successive induction. Strong tonic contraction of the extensor muscles to maintain the slightly crouched position in preparation for action increases the subsequent force of the quick coordinated movement which follows.

The eyes are closely associated with head movements in that they maintain the focus during movement. The head and extremities are linked so that eye-hand coordination can be facilitated and head movements may reinforce movements of the extremities. Integration of the total body in relation to space and time is important if efficiency of movement is desired.

REFERENCES

1. Campbell, E. J. M. "An Electromyographic Study of the Role of the Abdominal Muscles in Breathing," *J. Physiol.*, 117:222 (1952).

2. Duchenne, G. B. A. *Physiology of Motion* (trans. by E. B. Kaplan). Philadelphia: W. B. Saunders Co., 1959.

3. Floyd, W. F. and P. H. S. Silver. "Electromyographic Study of Patterns of Activity of the Anterior Abdominal Wall Muscles in Man," *J. Anat.*, 84:132 (1950).

4. Floyd, W. F. and P. H. S. Silver. "Function of Erectores Spinae in Flexion of the Trunk," *Lancet*, 1:133 (1951).

5. Floyd, W. F. and P. H. S. Silver. "The Function of the Erectores Spinae Muscles in Certain Movements and Postures in Man," *J. Physiol.*, 129:184 (1955).

6. Howorth, M. B. *Textbook of Orthopedics*. Philadelphia: W. B. Saunders Company (1959), chapter 5.

7. Partridge, M. J. and C. E. Walters. "Participation of the Abdominal Muscles in Various Movements of the Trunk in Man," *J. Am. Phys. Therapy Ass'n.*, 39:791 (1959).

8. Reeder, T. "Electromyographic Study of the Latissimus Dorsi Muscle," *J. Am. Phys. Therapy Ass'n.*, 43:165 (1963).

Mechanics of
Various Types
of Human Tasks

The tasks that must be performed in the course of everyday living, work, and recreation are extremely numerous and varied. In attempting to classify the various tasks into major categories consideration was given to the element(s) that differentiated a specific task from others, and the element(s) common to a group of tasks. The four categories chosen (support, suspension, production of force to move the body or objects, and absorption of force) are in no way mutually exclusive. Almost no task is purely supportive or purely suspension. Normally one stands to move; one hangs to perform some stunts that involve motion; and certainly one must move to receive force without injury. Thus tasks that involve the production of force cut across all of the other categories. However, there are certain problems unique to support, others that are unique to suspension, and still others unique to situations that require the individual to receive a force. There are certain elements that make a suspension task basically different from a supportive task. Thus the following discussion contains four main sections: supportive tasks, suspension tasks, movement tasks, and tasks involving receiving force.

SUPPORTIVE TASKS

Tasks of the human body may involve supporting the body itself on a more or less solid surface or in water. The body may be supported in a horizontal or a vertical position with either the feet or head downward. Support of the body itself may be the primary purpose as when standing, sitting, lying, or kneeling, although usually it is for the purpose of making certain movements possible. The body must be held in an upright position to walk, run, or throw with any degree of force. In fact there is a supportive element in any position or movement. Besides supporting the body itself, this type of task may involve holding an object. This again may be a static support simply holding, or, more usually, may involve holding the object while it is being moved (carried or lifted). While an object may be suspended from the body, some part of the object (e.g., its handle or an attached rope) must be supported. When a suitcase is "suspended" from the hand the fingers under the handle actually function to support it.

The physical laws of gravity, buoyancy, equilibrium, leverage, and force operate in all supportive tasks. Since the force of gravity constantly acts on all objects, it must be considered in the determination of any position or movement and thus in any task. This force acts on all parts of any object in a vertically downward direction. The center of weight of an object, or the point about which the object balances, is called *the center of gravity* and the line from this point vertically downward is called the *line of gravity*. For all practical purposes the center of gravity of an adult standing with the arms hanging at the sides can be considered to be centered in the upper hip region. The exact location varies with body build and, in general, because of the heavier shoulders and lighter hips of males, their centers of gravity are at a slightly higher point than are those of females.

SUPPORT OF THE BODY ITSELF
ON A SURFACE

For any object to be balanced, its center of gravity must be above its base of support. Thus, in standing, the center of gravity of the total body must be over the feet. However, since the body is not one solid object but rather a series of irregularly shaped segments held together by muscles and ligaments, the balance of the various segments of the body also must be considered.

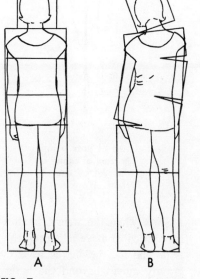

A   B   A   B

FIG. 6.   **FIG. 7.**

Antero-posterior view of standing position. A. Each body segment balanced above segment below. B. Zig-zag posture.

Back view of standing position. A. Each body segment balanced above the segment below. B. Zig-zag position as result of standing with weight on left foot.

The segments of the body must be centered one above the other if the standing position is to be maintained without undue strain. The muscles and ligaments, and in some cases the pressure on the bony structure, prevent the segments from falling apart if the center of gravity of one segment is not above its base, but this causes strain on muscles or ligaments and pressure in joints as well as making it necessary to place a counterbalancing segment off-center in the opposite direction to keep the center of gravity of the total body over the base made by the feet (Figs. 6 and 7).

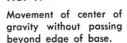

FIG. 8.
Line of gravity falls in front of center of the knee and in front of ankle.

FIG. 9.
Movement of center of gravity without passing beyond edge of base.

Since when the weight is close to the edge of the base, little movement is required to move it *beyond* the base, the body is unstable when the weight is on the toes or on the heels even though it is balanced *until* the line of gravity moves beyond the base. When the center of gravity is above the *center* of the base, movement is possible *in any direction* before the line of gravity falls outside the base, and thus the body is more stable. Therefore, the best standing position is that in which each segment is centered over the segment immediately below (its supporting base) and the body weight as a whole is centered over the base made by the feet. The body can sway forward and backward without the line of gravity falling beyond the heels or the toes. Hellebrandt (2) found that when standing, individuals are constantly swaying and that this involuntary swaying is important in that it aids the return of venous blood and assures adequate circulation to the brain.

When the weight is centered over the base, the line of gravity falls forward of the center of the knee and in front of the ankle, and therefore gravity constantly tends to rotate the body forward around the ankle (Fig. 8). However, if the line of gravity fell *through* the ankles so that this rotating force would be removed, it would be precariously near the back edge of the base (heels). The muscular effort needed to maintain the stable posture with the weight centered over the feet is imposed on the large and powerful calf muscles, while the weaker anterior group is released from counterbalancing tension (3). This position is also important in the initiation of forward movement (3) (see moving the body, p. 57).

When the base is larger, the center of gravity can move further before passing beyond the edge of the base. Thus, in general, spreading the feet apart contributes to stability (Fig. 9). However, no one physical law can be applied without consideration of other factors that may be introduced. If, when standing, the feet are spread a few inches sideways (the width of the hips), the legs are vertical and the force exerted by the weight of the body is straight down on the floor giving a straight upward reaction force to support the body. If, on the other hand, the feet are spread *more* than the width of the hips the force against the floor becomes a diagonal one with both downward and outward components (Fig. 10). Providing there is sufficient friction to resist the outward component, the balance is not

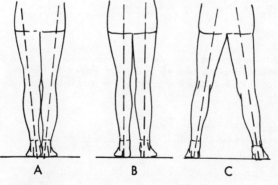

A   **B**   **C**

FIG. 10.

A. Forces exerted at a slightly inward angle. B. Forces exerted straight downward. C. Forces exerted at an outward angle. (Drawing adapted from Broer, Marion R., *Efficiency of Human Movement*. Philadelphia: W. B. Saunders Company, 1966, p. 114.)

impaired but a greater number of muscles must contract to maintain the position and, depending on the purpose of the task, considerable energy may be wasted. When there is not sufficient friction between the feet and the supporting surface (e.g., standing on ice), spreading the feet farther than the width of the hips so that an outward component of force is introduced makes the body less stable despite the larger base. When the outward component of the force is not resisted by friction the feet continue to slide

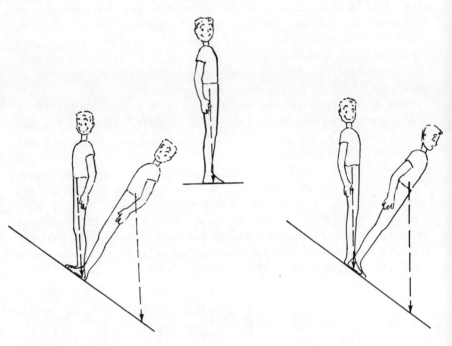

FIG. 11.

Adjustment of body angle at ankle region to keep center of gravity above base when standing on incline. (Drawing adapted from Broer, Marion R., *Efficiency of Human Movement,* Philadelphia: W. B. Saunders Company, 1966, p. 135.)

outward. Therefore, when standing, the most efficient position is that with the feet directly under the hips. This gives as large a base as possible without introducing any diagonal forces.

When standing on an incline the body weight must be moved forward if the incline is upward and backward if the incline is downward. If the same relationship between the lower legs and feet were maintained, the line of gravity would fall outside the base (Fig. 11). Adjustment of the body weight as a unit from the ankle region makes it possible to maintain the well-balanced alignment of the various body segments.

Since a lower center of gravity can move farther than a high center of gravity before the line of gravity falls outside the base, a low center of gravity also contributes to stability. Thus the body is most stable in a supine or prone position, since its center of gravity is only a few inches above a very large base. When lying on the side it is much less stable, since its base is small from front to back. It can be made stable by placing one hand on the supporting surface a few inches in front of the trunk, or by bending one knee and thus enlarging the base in the direction of the instability. Sitting and kneeling are more stable positions than standing but less stable than lying flat, both because of height of center of gravity and size of base.

When shoes with small high heels are worn the center of gravity is raised, the base narrowed, and the weight thrown forward. Thus stability is greatly impaired and there must be an adjustment at the ankle region which draws the weight backward to keep the body balanced above the feet.

The eyes and ears are extremely important in the balance of the body and the reflexes discussed earlier must be considered (see Reflexes, p. 15). Except in cases where there is an abnormality, the organs of the middle ear (semicircular canals) are more important in movement than in supportive tasks.

The body can support itself in an inverted position on the hand(s) or the head and hands. When the body is supported by the head and hands (head-stand) placed in a triangular relationship, the base is relatively large both forward-backward and side to side. If the segments of the body are aligned one above the other and the line of gravity of the total body falls over the center of this base, the position is stable (Fig. 12). The hands, being forward of the center of gravity of the body, are in a position to apply force backward-upward if the body should start to fall forward. Through use of the fingers the hand affords good leverage not afforded by the head which forms the back edge of the base; therefore any tendency of the center of gravity to fall forward is more easily controlled than a tendency to fall backward. When only the hands comprise the base of support (hand stand) the base is very narrow forward-backward and the center of gravity is raised resulting in an extremely unstable position.

SUPPORT OF THE BODY ITSELF IN WATER

When an object is submerged in water instead of surrounded by air, the force of buoyancy in effect supports the body. *Archimedes' principle* states that a body wholly or partially submerged in a fluid is buoyed up by a force equal to the weight of the displaced fluid. This force acts in an *upward* direction and, depending on the weight and size of the object, counteracts to varying degrees the force of gravity. Since the relationship of size to weight is not the same for all of the segments of the human body, the various parts are

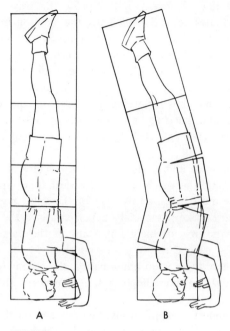

FIG. 12.

Headstand. A. Each body segment centered above segment below. B. Zig-zag position of segments.

pushed upward by different amounts of force. The chest region containing the lungs, which are filled with air, is very light for its size and is usually the most buoyant part of the body. Therefore, this is normally the point about which an individual balances when in the water. The legs, because they are primarily muscle and bone, tend to be heavy for their size and usually sink, since the force of buoyancy is not great enough to offset gravity (the legs weigh more than a corresponding volume of water). Also the legs are long and the center of weight of this segment (the two legs) is far from the chest, making leverage a factor which increases the effect of their weight. Thus when lying motionless in the water the chest region is supported and the legs drop downward until the center of gravity of the body is directly under the center of buoyancy (the most buoyant point of the body) (1). When floating in the water most individuals are supported in an angled position. If the legs are large and, because of the presence of considerable adipose tissue, their weight is less than that of an equal volume of water, they are supported at the surface of the water. If the body build is such that the total body is heavier than an equal volume of water (very muscular and compact) it will not be supported in the water but will sink until it rests on the bottom of the pool.

SUPPORT OF AN OBJECT
BY THE BODY

When an external weight is supported by the body it affects the center of gravity of the body. In effect it becomes a part of the body and the center of gravity which must be kept above the base is that of the body plus the weight. Because the object "overweights" the body on the side of the supported weight, the new center of gravity shifts to a position between the center of gravity of the body alone and the center of gravity of the weight. The body must be shifted away from the weight to bring the new center of gravity back over the center of the base if balance is to be maintained. The heavier the weight or the farther from the body's center of gravity it is held, the farther is this new center of gravity (body-plus-weight) from the body's center of gravity and the greater is the shift required. When carrying a heavy sack of groceries in front of the body, the weight of the sack causes the center of gravity of the sack-plus-body to be forward of the center of weight of the body alone, and the body must be shifted backward to keep this new center of gravity over the feet (Fig. 13). If a suitcase is carried in the right hand the center of gravity of the suitcase and body is to the right of that of the body alone and to keep this point above the feet the body must be shifted to the left. When these adjustments are made from the ankle region the balance of the various body segments is not disturbed. The total body weight is used to counterbalance the weight of the object. Pregnancy involves carrying a weight in front of the body and displaces the center of gravity forward. When the adjustment to the added weight is made from the waist, strain is put on the structures of the lower back with resultant backache. The strain becomes increasingly greater as the pregnancy progresses because of the additional weight. If a backward adjustment is made from the ankle region, the weight of body as a unit counterbalances the added weight in front bringing the center of gravity of the total (body plus the added weight) back over the feet without additional strain of the lower back.

Just as the body's center of gravity must be above its feet for it to remain in balance, a held object's center of gravity must be above the base made by the hand(s) or whatever body part supports it. Even though a suitcase is suspended, the center of its handle is above the hand or fingers holding it. Since gravity is pulling downward on the object, an upward force must be applied to hold it. When the hand or segment holding the object is placed under it, the force can be applied in direct opposition to gravity and therefore is most effective. If, on the other hand, the object is held between the thumb and fingers (pincer position, Fig. 14A), the forces are exerted inward toward the object and only friction between the object and

FIG. 13.

Center of gravity of body-plus-weight falls between center of gravity of body and center of gravity of held object.

a. line of gravity of object
b. line of gravity of body
c. line of gravity of body-plus-object

fingers and thumb keeps gravity from pulling the object downward. Unless the fingers can be curved around some part of the object so that they form a base *under* it, the supportive force is not applied in the direction that resists gravity (the force acting on the object), and considerable force must be applied by the relatively weak muscles of the thumb and fingers; thus this is an inefficient method of holding. Carrying even a light sack between fingers and thumb for any length of time is difficult. Thus the top of the sack is rolled to make a handle *under* which the fingers can be placed (Fig. 14B).

Application of the leverage principles is extremely important in any holding task. Since the effect of a weight is increased when it is supported farther from the body, a book that can be held easily on the palm close to the shoulder becomes heavy when held at arm's length out from the shoulder. The downward force exerted by the book equals its weight multiplied by the distance from the shoulder (the axis for the lever which is the arm). Thus when the book is held at arm's length the downward force which it exerts is much greater than that of the same book held close to the shoulder. It is easier to carry a suitcase, box, etc., by a handle that the fingers can wrap around and thus exert upward force than by holding it with the hands under the center of the box itself. Its center of gravity can be kept closer to the body and its weight can be balanced by a lean of the total body to the opposite side or by lifting the opposite arm. The latter

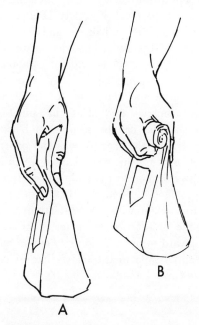

FIG. 14.

Holding a sack. A. Between thumb and fingers (pincer position). B. Top of sack rolled to make surface *under* which fingers can be placed.

FIG. 15.

Hunching of shoulder to support strap of bag.

movement increases the effectiveness of the weight of that arm in counterbalancing the box because it is then farther from the body. A relatively flat object such as a suitcase can be held more easily when tipped onto its side rather than flat because this places its center of gravity closer to the body and reduces its leverage. However, if the object is very wide and has no handle, tipping it onto its side raises its center of gravity and may introduce a balance problem. Since a tray of dishes cannot be tipped, it is supported above one shoulder so that its center of weight is as close to the body's line of gravity as possible. One hand is placed under the center of gravity of the tray to exert force upward to oppose gravity and the other, placed at the edge of the tray, is in a good position to control any tipping. A relatively small amount of force at the edge, either up if that side becomes overbalanced, or down to balance the opposite edge if it begins to fall, is effective; being at the edge of the tray, the leverage for that hand is increased.

An object can be supported by a strap over the shoulder more successfully by a man than a woman. Since most women's shoulders are not as square as those of most men, but slope downward, the strap slides off the shoulder unless the tip is rotated upward to give a horizontal base that can apply force directly upward to resist the force of gravity (Fig. 15). This position of the shoulder girdle throws it out of balance and results in a curve of the upper spine to the side of the lifted shoulder. Most women cannot support a purse by a strap over the shoulder without assuming this hunched shoulder position, and if it is assumed consistently, stretchng of the muscles on the outside of the curve and shortening of those on the inside with accompanying strain of muscles and stress in spinal joints result. This same hunching of one shoulder can be seen when books and other objects are carried in one arm against the chest. Books and papers can be most efficiently held in a briefcase, because this has a handle which allows the fingers to exert force straight upward close to the body's line of gravity.

Whatever the holding task, the problem is essentially that of determining how the body can counterbalance the weight with the least strain and how the segment which must support the object can exert force through the object's center of gravity straight upward in order to *directly* oppose gravity and still keep the weight as close as possible to the body's line of gravity to reduce its leverage advantage.

REFERENCES

1. Broer, Marion R. *Efficiency of Human Movement.* Philadelphia: W. B. Saunders Company, 1966, pp. 310–11.

2. Hellebrandt, Frances A. and Elizabeth Brogdon. "The Hydrostatic Effect of Gravity on Circulation in Supported, Unsupported and Suspended Positions," *Am. J. Physiol.,* 123:95–96 (1938).

3. Morton, J. Dudley and Dudley Dean Fuller. *Human Locomotion and Body Form.* Baltimore: The Williams & Wilkins Co., 1952, p. 50.

SUSPENSION TASKS

Rarely does an individual suspend himself for the purpose of suspension only; movement almost always is involved. Therefore, examples of the movement problems involved in such tasks are discussed in this section. The number of suspension tasks which the human body must perform are relatively few and, except for children's play or emergencies, most of them are involved in body conditioning exercises or gymnastic techniques. Children travel hand over hand on a bar or a tree limb with feet dangling in the air, or they hang by their lower extremities. Those of all ages who are interested in increasing the strength of the muscles in the arms and shoulders hang from a bar and attempt to chin themselves. Gymnasts perform a variety of movements on the horizontal bar (women on uneven parallel bars also), some of which involve suspension of the body and others, support of the body. They also perform on the rings and ropes, sometimes suspending the body and sometimes supporting it on the hands which grasp the rings. Obviously all suspension tasks must have an element of support. When hanging, some part of the body, usually the fingers, must be above the supporting surface—

tree limb, bar, rings, etc. However, the fact that gravity pulls the body downward from the surface changes considerably the problems of this type of task from those of tasks which require the individual to hold the many segments of the body upright against gravity's pull. Some tasks such as hanging from the rings are primarily suspension while some, such as standing on the hands on the rings, are primarily supportive and involve all the balance problems discussed previously.

Although when any movement is involved the vestibular mechanism and the eyes are active in orienting the body and head in space (see Reflexes, p. 15), in pure suspension tasks balance is not a problem; gravity pulls the body straight downward from the point of contact. The first problem is one of applying sufficient force to stabilize the body segment which is above the supporting surface. When hanging by the hands, the hands must be stabilized in a grasping position. Hands may grasp a bar with the palms facing forward (forearms pronated) or with palms facing toward the body (forearms supinated). In a study of the use of these two positions, Gala (1) found that college women's performance on the modified pull-up and bent-arm hang tests was better during tests executed with a supinated grip. There was some indication that the pronated grip may require more action of the left biceps, left brachioradialis, and right and left deltoid to execute the modified pull-ups and of the right and left trapezius and right and left posterior deltoid to execute the bent-arm hang. In the bent-arm hang there was some indication of more action in the left triceps when the supinated grip was employed.

The second problem in a suspension task is to apply the force required to *move* the body from the straight suspended position. For those tasks that involve a solid surface such as a bar, the individual can simply hang straight down; he can move along the bar by moving one hand and then the other; or he can swing around the bar. To accomplish the "walking" along the bar, it is necessary to produce force to move a hand and to avoid a dropping of that side of the body which is below the moving hand. This can be done by, immediately before release, producing upward force with the hand and arm to be moved by flexing that elbow and pulling downward on the top of the bar. This lifts that side of the body and as the body weight is momentarily removed from the hand, it can be moved. If a greater upward force is applied, the legs swing to that side and upward. As gravity pulls them down again they gain momentum which, because of inertia makes the movement tend to continue beyond the midline, swinging the legs to the opposite side and, with very little force, that hand can then be moved. In this way the individual can progress along a bar. This pendular motion is used to advantage in the performance of the traveling rings. In those techniques which involve circling a bar with the hands as the contact point, the force to lift the body up around the bar usually results from inertia, the momentum of the body drop. The force of gravity, momentum, and inertia are used to produce the movement required for the performance of many techniques.

Tasks that involve suspension from freely moving objects, such as ropes or rings, demand more control since any momentum gained by the body is transferred to the supporting object. A great deal more muscular effort is required to stabilize the object. This is required in the performance of many techniques on the rings. When the object from which the body is suspended is free to move, the equal and opposite forces required for the movement of the body will not always result from the application of body force. When performing on the rings, the arm and shoulder muscles must exert force to hold the rings steady, making a resistive surface so that as other body forces are applied against this resistive surface a reaction force will cause body motion in the desired direction.

REFERENCES

1. Gala, Rosemary. "The Effect of Two Gripping Positions on Performance of College Women on the Modified Pull-up and the Bent-arm Hang Tests and the Action of Selected Arm and Shoulder Girdle Muscles as Indicated by Electromyography," Unpublished Master's Thesis, University of Washington, 1965.

MOVEMENT TASKS

MOVING THE BODY

Whether the body is producing force to move itself or some body segment, or to resist or react to an external force, the force for the movement or resistance must be supplied by muscles innervated by nerves. For movement to occur, the force produced by the muscles must be sufficient to overcome the inertia of the body or the body segment (its tendency to retain its present state of motion). The amount of force which is produced beyond this, determines the speed with which the body (or segment) moves. Newton's First Law of Motion states that an object at rest or in motion will remain at rest or in motion at the same speed and in the same direction unless acted upon by a force (Law of Inertia). To move an object which is at rest the force must be greater than the weight of the object. The heavier the object and the faster it is moving, the greater the force required to change its speed or direction (Newton's Second Law of Motion). Thus once the body or any segment of the body has started to move, it is easier to keep it moving, and the faster it is moving the more difficult it is to stop the motion.

When the human body is moved as a whole in a plane, car, or boat, for example, it is said to experience *linear* motion; all parts of the body move in the same direction and for the same distance in the same amount of time. Also, it is possible for the human body to move itself linearly by means of rotary motion of some of its segments or of the entire body. Since when a body segment is moved it rotates about a joint (an axis), it undergoes *rotary motion*. When walking, the entire body moves from one point in space to another as a result of the rotary motion of the legs about the hip joints. In the performance of a forward roll the body moves linearly as a result of rotary motion of the entire body both around its center of gravity and around successive points of contact with the mat.

Since muscles exert force by shortening, the force exerted by them is a pull. For effectiveness the pull must be executed from a firm base. For example, if when pushing the body away from a wall, the scapulae were not held solidly against the ribs but were allowed to move outward when the hands push against the wall, the upper body would not move away from the wall. In this case the shoulder girdle is the base for the force, and if it is not held firmly against the ribs (if the base for the pushing force moves), the purpose of the force application (moving the body away from the wall) cannot be accomplished. When any segment(s) of the body is (are) to be moved, the base for the movement must be stabilized. This is accomplished by concurrent contraction of muscles other than those causing the desired movement. The force of this contraction must be sufficient to hold the segment in position but not to move it.

The tasks that involve moving various segments of the body, or moving the entire body, involve the same principles for the maintenance of stability as do the supportive tasks. However, some additional problems are involved. Although the center of gravity of the human body in normal standing position with the arms along the sides is approxmately centered in the upper hip region, any movement of a body segment shifts this center of gravity, sometimes causing it to fall outside the base made by the feet. When it falls outside the base made by the feet, the individual, like any other object, is pulled downward by gravity and tends to fall until a new base is established under its center of gravity. The human body differs from other objects in that it has a nervous system that causes autonomous adjustments to be made in response to changes in the body's center of gravity. Whenever any part of the body moves away from the line of gravity of the total body, the center of gravity of the body shifts in the direction of that movement, and the total body or another segment must move in the opposite direction to bring the center of gravity back over the center of the base. When the arms are raised forward to shoulder height, the center of gravity shifts forward and upward in the body and an autonomous adjustment is made to move the total body backward to counterbalance the weight of the forward arms (Fig. 16A). If this adjustment is consciously inhibited the weight falls precariously near, or may fall even beyond, the forward edge of the base. Since in the forward position the arms are farther from the center of the body than when hanging at the sides, the effect of their weight is augmented (see Leverage Discussion, p. 44). If the arms are moved upward to a point straight up from the shoulders, the center of gravity of the body is again along the same line as when the arms are along the sides but it is located higher in the body and the individual is somewhat less stable (Fig. 16B). If the trunk is flexed forward, the center of gravity of the total body moves forward-downward and the line of gravity falls beyond the toes. The individual unconsciously counterbalances the weight of the trunk, shoulders, upper extremities, and head by moving the hips backward (Fig. 16C). If standing with his back close to a wall so that this autonomous adjustment is impossible, he must move a foot forward to establish a new base under the forward center of gravity or he will fall downward. Much of the adjustment to balance the movement of body segments occurs at the reflex level and thus takes place without the individual's awareness.

In all movement tasks various segments of the body are constantly moving, and therefore the center of gravity is constantly shifting, sometimes even to a point which is outside the body itself, as when an individual reaches forward to touch his toes or pikes in a dive (Fig. 16C, D). In such cases the center of gravity of the body as a whole lies in the space between the forward flexed trunk and the thighs.

It was stated earlier that in general the larger the base the more stable the object. However, it does not improve stability if the base is enlarged in one direction and the center of gravity is moved back and forth in another direction. When swinging the arms forward and backward the center of gravity moves forward-backward and the feet must be spread in a forward-backward stride if the center of gravity is to remain over the base. If the feet were spread sideways the base would still be small in the direction that the weight of the body is moving. *Therefore, in making the base larger for stability the direction of the movement involved must be considered.* When the feet are spread forward-backward the pelvic girdle is rotated, to the left if the right foot is forward and to the right if the left foot is forward. Therefore, movements which involve trunk rotation to the right are more easily performed when the left foot is forward, but movements involving rotation to the left are restricted. The opposite is true when the left foot

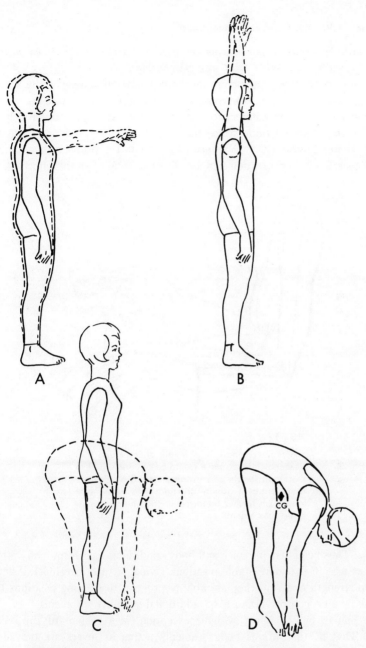

FIG. 16.

A. Reflex adjustment to movement of center of gravity forward due to lifting arms forward. B. No adjustment forward-backward required with arms overhead (center of gravity higher). C. Reflex adjustment to movement of center of gravity forward due to bending forward-downward. D. Pike position. Note center of gravity outside body.

is forward. *Therefore, when making the base wider the effect of the position on the restriction of joints must also be considered.*

Because of the many balance problems encountered whenever the various body segments are moved (the more vigorously they are moved the greater the problems) many exercises can be more effective when performed in lying, sitting, or kneeling positions. Since these positions afford a larger base and a lower center of gravity, they reduce or eliminate the problem of maintaining balance, and concentration can be directed wholly to the effort of the

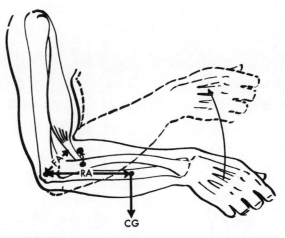

FIG. 17.

Schematic comparison of length of force arm (FA, perpendicular distance from line of muscle pull to axis) and length of resistance arm (RA, distance from center of gravity of segment to axis). Note how much farther hand moves than point of muscular attachment.

exercise. Thus beginners in dance and body conditioning perform many strong exercises first in the more stable positions (lying, sitting, kneeling). As they develop strength and skill they are able to progress to starting positions that require greater control because of additional stability problems.

The human body, almost without exception, is a system of third class levers. That is, the various body segments acting as levers are moved by forces applied nearer to the joints (axis of rotation) than the center of gravity of the segment to be moved. Therefore, the force arm (the perpendicular distance from the muscle to the axis) is shorter than the weight arm (the distance from the center of gravity of the segment to be moved to the axis). Since the effectiveness of the force (or weight) depends upon the *amount of force* (or weight) *multiplied by its distance from the axis* for the movement, the muscular force operates at a disadvantage. If the muscles that flex the elbow were attached so that the perpendicular distance from the muscle (line of force) to the joint were one-third as far from the elbow (axis for movement) as the center of gravity of the forearm were from the elbow, it would require a force three times the weight of the forearm to hold the arm up against gravity's pull and more than this to move it (Fig. 17). However, during the motion the hand at the end of the arm moves much farther than the point of muscular attachment and thus, since the total forearm is moving for the same length of time, the hand moves much faster than the point where the force is exerted (point of muscular attachment). On the whole the body segments (levers) are long and therefore, the distal

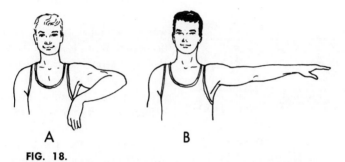

A   **B**

FIG. 18.

A. Arm lifted with elbow well bent. B. Arm lifted with elbow straight.

ends move rapidly. This means that the human body is a machine which can produce considerable speed but is not effective in moving great weight. To move heavy weights without strain the body employs outside implements. In general, movement of the segments of the body does not involve great weights. However, when a segment is lengthened, its center of gravity is farther from the axis and, therefore, it takes more force to move it. The difference in the force required as the lever is lengthened can be felt when the arm is lifted to shoulder height, first with the elbow well bent and then with the elbow straight (Fig. 18). If the arm is held at shoulder height for a period of time, the greater effort required to hold the longer lever (elbow straight) is even more obvious. Because of the length and weight of the trunk, shoulder girdle, upper extremities, neck and head, holding the trunk up in a standing forward-bent position for any length of time places a strain on the structures of the relatively weak lower back (Fig. 19). In doing a sit-up the center of gravity of the upper body is farthest from the hips (the axis for the movement) at the very beginning of the movement. As the upper body is moved toward the vertical position, the perpendicular distance from its center of gravity to the hips becomes increasingly shorter, and therefore, the effort required is less. It is also less because of the momentum which has been developed. It is at the moment when the exercise is started and the inertia of the upper body must be overcome, that the muscles must operate at the greatest leverage disadvantage (1). Rather than using an exercise which places the greatest strain on the muscles at the beginning of the movement and progressively less as the exercise continues, it would be wise to reverse the exercise, that is to start in a sitting position and lower the upper body in a curled position to a 45 degree angle (approximately) with the floor and hold this position for about six seconds. To increase the difficulty of the exercise, the angle at which the upper body is held can be decreased. When lying on the back with the arms stretched overhead along the floor, the sit-up requires relatively little effort of the abdominal muscles since a forceful swing of the arms upward-forward produces momentum which is transferred to the trunk and greatly aids in overcoming its inertia.

FIG. 19.

Strain on lower back when leaning forward for any length of time.

Many tasks involve moving the body as a whole (linearly) along a more or less solid surface (walking, running, skipping, sliding, galloping, etc.). While the force that *actually* moves the body comes from some surface, this force results only as a reaction to a force produced by the body itself against the surface. Since to every action force there is an equal and opposite reaction force (Newton's Third Law), the surface applies an opposite force against the body and this is the force which causes the body to move. When the hands are placed against the wall and pushed forward, the wall applies a backward force against the body and the body moves backward away from the wall. When the center of gravity is forward of the pushing foot, the foot pushes backward and downward against the floor and the floor pushes forward-upward against the body (Fig. 20A). The force is applied in the direction of a line from the foot applying the force through the center of gravity of the body. This diagonally forward-upward force is, in effect, the resultant of two forces. The *upward* component of the force is effective in supporting the body against gravity's pull while it moves forward as a result of the *forward* component of the force. The greater the force exerted against the floor, the greater the reaction force against the body and the faster the body is moved forward (Newton's Second Law—when a body is acted on by a force, its resulting acceleration is proportional to the force).

In walking, the individual can reduce the force required by taking ad-

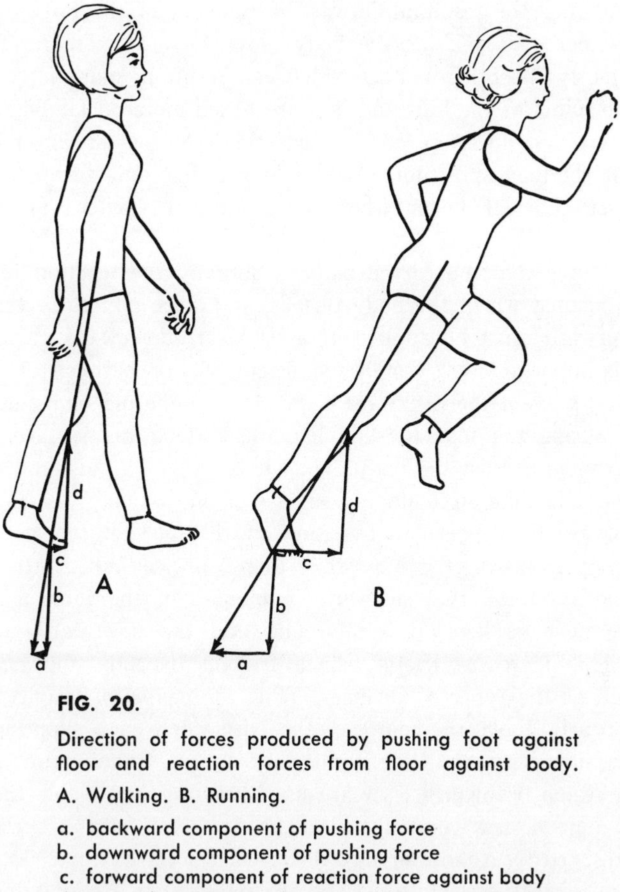

FIG. 20.

Direction of forces produced by pushing foot against floor and reaction forces from floor against body.

A. Walking. B. Running.

a. backward component of pushing force
b. downward component of pushing force
c. forward component of reaction force against body
d. upward component of reaction force against body

Note the greater forward component of the reaction force in running than in walking.

vantage of gravity. By shifting the center of gravity of the body forward of the edge of the base, gravity can be used to assist in overcoming inertia and a relatively small force is required to move the body forward. When the center of gravity of the total body is over the center of the base made by the feet, the line of gravity falls forward of the ankles (see Supportive Tasks, p. 39) and gravity exerts a forward rotating force on the body as a whole; therefore, relaxation of the extensor muscles results in movement of the center of gravity forward.

The more the force is exerted in the direction of the desired motion, the more effective is the force. Therefore, the body leans forward more in running than walking so that the backward component of the force against the floor and thus the resultant forward component of the force applied to the body is increased, making the body move forward more rapidly (Fig. 20B). Obviously the other factors which can result in more force are also applied. The joints of the hips and legs are flexed more on landing (see discussion of receiving force, p. 83) so that the extensors are stretched, and as they contract they apply force over a longer time and distance. Also the muscles must contract faster when more forceful (faster) movement is desired.

Since the force that moves the body is actually the reaction force from the surface against which the body pushes, and since any force that moves the body forward must be applied at a backward-downward angle to that surface, it is important that there be sufficient friction between the foot and the surface to prevent the backward component of the diagonal force of the foot from causing the foot to slide backward along the surface reducing the reactive force against the body. Thus it is easier to walk and run on a hard solid surface than on a slippery surface or one which gives. Sand which moves backward in response to the force of the foot returns less force to move the body forward. It is impossible to run on ice. When attempting to move the body on ice, the backward component of the force against the icy surface must be kept at a minimum and the downward component increased. This increases friction since friction depends upon *downward* force as well as the types of surfaces. Thus the center of gravity must be kept more nearly above the center of the base when on a slippery surface. This means that very small steps must be taken. Running on wet grass presents the same problem. Cleats are used because they pierce the surface and give a more or less vertical surface for applying force backward. This surface is resisted by a more or less vertical surface which applies an equal and opposite force directly forward and the reliance on friction is eliminated or considerably reduced (2).

In walking, speed is sacrificed to conservation of energy and control. Gravity can be used to advantage and since the body is moved relatively slowly, the force required to move it is minimal. Also the legs, and therefore the arms, do not need to be moved forward as rapidly and this again saves energy. Since the body moves forward relatively slowly, the forward foot strikes the ground well ahead of the body's center of gravity; until the center of gravity reaches the point above that foot, a diagonally *forward*-downward force is exerted by the foot against the ground which exerts a *backward*-upward reaction force against the body (Fig. 21). The backward component of this force resists the forward progress of the body and makes it possible to stop the body momentum at any point. In running, however, the foot strikes under (or nearly under) the center of gravity, and this makes faster movement possible, but the ability to stop the momentum suddenly, is lost.

While, in walking, the arms are swung forward straight (but relaxed) and legs are bent only enough to clear the ground easily, in running both arms and legs are bent considerably; the faster the pace, the greater the bend. When bent, the center of gravity of the extremity is much closer to the axis about which it is moving and therefore the effect of the weight of the extremity is lessened (leverage), and the arm or leg can be moved faster.

As the right leg swings forward to catch the forward moving weight, the pelvis is rotated toward the left. At the same time in order to balance this rotation and keep the resultant (or sum) of the forces straight ahead, the left arm swings forward rotating the shoulder girdle toward the right. This action of arms in opposition to that of the legs occurs in all movement and is controlled at the reflex level (see Reflexes, p. 15). However, it is possible to interfere with this reflex through conscious control of movement or through tension. Consciously directing attention to the alternation of the extremities frequently causes interference which disrupts the reflex pattern. Many an individual has found skipping difficult because he has been told to swing the left arm forward as the right knee is lifted. Consciously trying to do this may interfere with the reflex.

In all tasks which involve moving the body across a surface, the feet should be placed in the best position to apply force in a direction opposite to that of desired movement. When the toes are forward, in running or walking, the force is exerted straight backward but when they

FIG. 21.

Direction of force applied to floor by *forward* foot in walking and reaction force from floor against body.

a. forward component of force from foot
b. downward component of force from foot
c. backward component (resistive) of reaction force
d. upward component of reaction force

turn outward or inward the force is applied to an angle to the desired direction and therefore is not totally effective. Consideration must also be given to the direction of the forces through the joints of the body. When backward force is applied by the foot with the toes turned outward (or inward), the force moves diagonally across the arch of the foot, the ankle, and the knee. This puts a strain on these joints, which are not constructed to withstand heavy force against their sides, and injury frequently results.

A task may require that the body produce force to move itself while being supported by an object which itself is free to move. This means that the full force produced by the body will not be returned by the supporting surface, since some of it will be used in moving that surface itself. Swimming movements fall into this group of tasks, since the water through which the body moves is also the surface against which the force is applied by the body. Some of it is returned to move the body in the opposite direction and some moves the surface itself (the water) in the direction that the force is applied by the body. Canoeing and rowing are also this type of task as are some of the suspension tasks discussed previously (see Suspension Tasks, p. 49). More force must be applied or slower movement of the body results when the surface is nonresistive than when it is solid.

Some tasks involve the projection of the body itself through the air. In hopping, jumping, leaping, or diving the body becomes a projectile which moves through the air. It is given an initial force and then allowed to move under the influence of gravity. When the body itself is a projectile, air resistance is of lesser importance. The initial force and gravity are the two most important forces. Therefore, in a dive the path of the body's center of gravity through the air depends upon the force applied (by the rebound of the board, the extension of the lower extremities, and the arm lift) and the angle of the line from the center of gravity of the body to the feet at take-off. Although the position of various body segments may change while the body is in the air and this will shift the location of the center of gravity within the body, the path of the center of gravity itself cannot be altered after take-off (Fig. 22). It depends on the force applied and the angle of take-off.

If the purpose of the task is to move the body upward as far as possible, all force should be applied in this direction and this is accomplished when the center of gravity is directly over the feet at take-off. Since gravity is constantly acting to pull the body downward at a constant acceleration *which is independent of any horizontal motion of the body,* the body moves farthest *forward* when the take-off force is applied at a 45 degree angle. Half of the force is applied upward to resist gravity and keep the body in the air so that it can move forward, and half is applied in the direction of desired movement (forward). In jumping for distance it is necessary to move the center of gravity ahead of the feet before take-off. This can be accomplished by taking a starting position with the body weight over the forward edge of the base and the arms well back so that the trunk can be farther forward over the feet (balanced by the arms). When the arms are

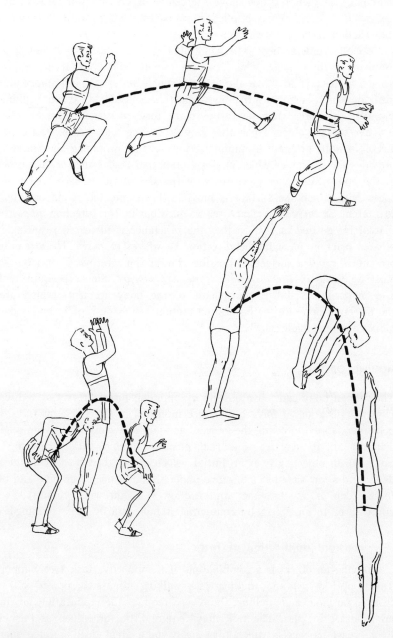

FIG. 22.

Path of center of gravity of body in various body projecting activities.

swung forward vigorously at take-off, both the momentum of the arms and the change in their position move the center of gravity well forward of the feet so that the force is applied in a backward-downward direction and the reaction force is forward-upward.

Normally, unless there is a wind blowing, air resistance is not a great problem in those tasks which involve moving the body itself. However, when the task is to move the body through water, the resistance of the medium which surrounds the body must be considered. When walking or running, the force that sends the body forward comes from the highly resistive surface along which the body is moving and the resistance of the air to forward progress is minimal. However, in swimming the water both provides the resistance which causes motion *and* resists the forward progress of the body. Resistance increases with the size of the surface area and the speed with which the surface is moving. Therefore, the swimmer attempts to present as *large a surface* area as possible in the direction *opposite* to that of his desired motion so that the resistance is increased resulting in a greater reaction force in the direction he wishes to move. He attempts to present as *small* a surface as possible during those recovery motions which must be made *in the direction of desired motion*. Since speed of motion also increases resistance, movements of the body segments which are in the direction opposite to the desired motion are made rapidly and recovery movements are made slowly.

MOVING OBJECTS

The human body can move objects by applying force directly or indirectly. Direct application of force can be accomplished in three general ways. The body can apply force to the object more or less constantly over a given distance and for a given time (i.e., pushing, pulling, lifting, carrying); it can hold an object, give it an initial velocity, and then break contact suddenly and allow the object to move under the influence of gravity and other forces such as air resistance and friction (i.e., throwing, rolling); it can apply force to an object by contacting it momentarily (i.e., striking) (3).

constant application of force

Carrying an object is a combination of a supportive task (see Supportive Tasks, pp. 43–46) and walking (see walking discussion, pp. 57–60). Effective pushing and pulling, however, require the application of many additional principles. The task may require little force such as pushing a light object on wheels which turn easily, or a great deal of force such as pushing a heavy piece of furniture which may or may not be on wheels. Because rolling friction is less than sliding friction, any wheels reduce the force required to move the object. The rolling friction of a hard wheel on a hard surface is less than that for a softer wheel and/or a softer surface. If the surface is soft the wheel causes an indentation and, in effect, builds a series of walls over which the object must move. If the wheel is soft, it is continuously flattened and therefore resists rolling (Fig. 23).

While force may be no problem in pushing or pulling a light object or an object on wheels moving over a solid surface, control of direction may cause difficulty. Through the application of leverage principles, the direction of a long light object's movement can be effectively controlled. By standing near the center of the object and spreading the hands to grasp it as far as possible on either side of the object's center of gravity, the lever arms of the forces which could rotate the object in either direction are lengthened and thus any tendency for the object to turn away from the straight path can be controlled with little effort, or the object can be turned easily if desired.

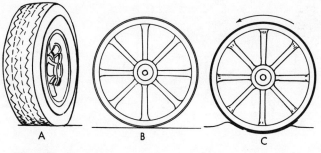

FIG. 23.

A. Soft wheel. B. Hard wheel and hard surface. C. Hard wheel and soft surface.

Heavy tasks may also need leverage for control as indicated for light tasks. However, in addition, all of the principles that lead to efficient force production must be employed. It is important to apply the force as much as possible in the direction of desired movement. To avoid placing the body in a position which is ineffective for its movement when pushing an object, the hands must usually be placed against the object at a point that is higher than its center of gravity. This means that while the force is exerted forward (in the direction of desired motion), it is applied above the center of gravity of the object. Thus the force tends to rotate the object around its base and some of the force is effective downward as well as forward. The additional downward-forward force increases friction and thus interferes with the movement of the object. In a few tasks such as pushing a broom, vacuum cleaner, or lawn mower, a downward component of the force increases the effectiveness for the particular purpose. When the object is on a relatively hard wheel or wheels (wheelbarrow, for example), friction is inconsequential. However, in many tasks the downward component of the force should be reduced to a minimum or eliminated, if possible. This can be done by pulling instead of pushing because when pulling the force is normally diagonally forward-upward. The upward component of the pulling force is effective in reducing friction. Up to a point the greater the upward component the more the friction is reduced. Since the pull is applied to the front of the object, if the angle is upward enough to lift the front and thus throw additional weight on the back edge, friction will not be decreased. Also the greater the upward angle, the smaller the forward component of the force, that portion of the force which is effective in moving the object in the desired direction. In general, *the more the force is applied in the direction of desired movement the more effective the force.* Therefore, to move a heavy object that is too

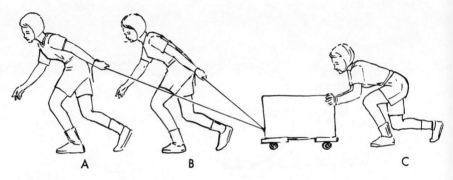

FIG. 24.

Pulling and pushing. A. High proportion of force effective in forward direction. B. Greater proportion of force effective in upward direction, less in forward direction. C. Ineffective position required to push low object.

low to easily apply forward force through its center of gravity by pushing, it is more efficient to pull the object with a rope; and the longer the rope, the higher the proportion of the force that will be effective in moving the object forward (Fig. 24). It follows that, *up to a point,* the greater the friction the more the rope would need to be shortened to increase the upward component of the force. It must be remembered that when pulling, the individual cannot see the load without turning. Whether it is more efficient to push or to pull depends upon the purpose and difficulty of the particular task.

Regardless of whether the task involves pushing or pulling, the principles which dictate efficient body position and movement are identical. In order to apply the force in the direction of desired movement the feet should be pointed in the direction of the movement and the center of gravity of the body must be ahead of the pushing foot. Therefore, the body must lean forward. To maintain the alignment of the body segments this lean is made from the ankle region (Fig. 25). The position of body lean from the ankle region results in the force which is applied by the extension of the joints of the lower extremities moving in a straight line diagonally upward-forward through the hips and trunk. If the shoulders and arms are stabilized, this force will be transferred through the arms to the object. If the body is bent forward at the hips, the knees and ankles are less flexed, thus less force can be produced by them and the force is more upward against the hips rather than forward-upward *through* the hips.

When pushing, the feet must be well back of the object to allow for a forward body lean so that the force can be exerted in a backward-downward direction against the floor resulting in a forward-upward reaction force through the body. When standing close to the object it is impossible to get the body's center of gravity ahead of the pushing foot. In order to maintain balance, the base must be widened in the forward direction and thus one foot is placed well forward of the other. Since more force can be produced

FIG. 25.

Pushing. Good body alignment; pushing force produced by legs.

by stronger muscles, the strongest muscles available for the pushing task (the legs) should be used. To place the leg muscles in a position which makes possible the application of considerable force against the floor (which is in return applied against the foot by the floor), the joints of the legs (ankles, knees, hips) must be bent. This puts them in a position of stretch and also makes possible extension, and thus forces production, over a period of time. The force exerted by the floor in response to the push of the feet, moves through the trunk and arms to the object being pushed; therefore the muscles of the trunk, shoulders, and arms must be set to resist the push of the object against them as the force produced by the body encounters the inertia of the object. To avoid a "give" in any part of the body which would absorb some force and result in less effective force against the object, all muscles contract together for a heavy task.

Once the object has begun to move, it takes less force to keep it moving,

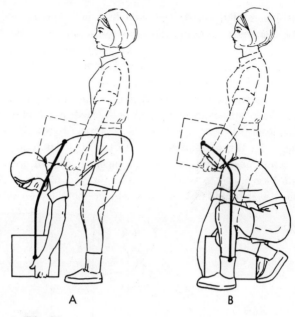

FIG. 26.

Lifting. A. Poor leverage; direction of force up and then in; major lifting force produced by back. B. Weight close to body's line of gravity; direction of force upward (curved arrow indicates movement of box to front as body rotates when left foot is brought back in line with right); force for lift produced by legs.

since an object in motion tends to remain in motion unless acted upon by another force (inertia). Friction, of course, is a force tending to stop the motion and therefore, unless some force is applied continuously the object is stopped by friction.

Lifting is a combination of pulling and pushing in a vertical direction and all the same principles apply. It is pulling when the object is below the shoulders and pushing when it is above. To avoid strain, the strongest muscles (the legs) should be used for heavy lifting tasks. Again, this means bending the joints of the legs to contact the load and setting the muscles of the trunk, shoulders, and arms so that the force produced by the leg extension will pass through them to the object.

Since the movement is vertically upward, the center of gravity must be centered over the base so that the force will be upward. In bending the legs, the movement of body segments is forward and backward and therefore, some widening of the base in a forward-backward direction makes it easier to keep the center of gravity centered above the base. However, since the object is supported by the body, an additional adjustment of the base may be required, a widening in the direction of the object because the center of gravity of the body-plus-weight must be considered also. The closer the weight is kept to the line of gravity of the body, the less its leverage effect and the less it moves the center of gravity from the body's normal line of gravity, and the easier it is to balance and to lift (see leverage discussion, p. 44). When an object is lifted by bending forward from the hips, balance is difficult because of the high and forward center of gravity and the small base. The lift must be in a backward-upward direction rather than straight upward, and the weight is far out from the axis of rotation (the hips) (Fig. 26A). In the forward bent position the weight pulls downward on the shoulders which are far from the hips. Thus strain of the structures of the lower back may result, since they are called upon to perform a heavy task under conditions of unfavorable leverage, unfavorable direction of force, and poor balance.

Balance of the object itself must also be considered in lifting tasks. This has been discussed under supportive tasks (see pp. 43–46).

Because the human body itself is a system of third class levers, it must make use of implements that are first or second class levers to gain a force advantage in the performance of heavy tasks. Whether the axis falls between the point of force application and the weight (first class) (Fig. 27A) or at the end of the lever, the force arm must be longer than the weight arm if a force advantage is to be gained. This is the situation when the

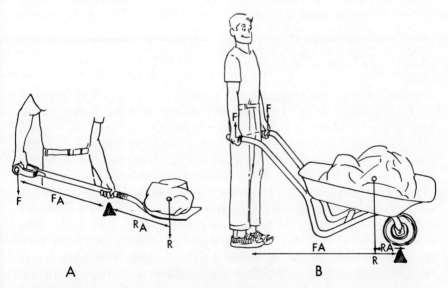

FIG. 27.

A. Shovel used as first class lever. B. Wheelbarrow used as second class lever.

weight is between the axis and the force (second class) (Fig. 27B). The
effectiveness of a force applied by the body can be greatly increased by
use of a crowbar (first class lever), since the distance from the point of force
application is far from the axis about which the bar rotates when the force
is applied. At the same time the effect of the weight to be lifted is kept
at a minimum because it is close to the axis of rotation. The handles of a
wheel barrow containing a considerable weight can be lifted because the
force is applied much farther from the axis (the wheel) than the center of
gravity of the load is located (second class lever).

development of momentum and sudden release

Many tasks involve projecting an object—that is, giving it an initial velocity
and allowing it to move under the influence of gravity, air resistance, and
friction. An object may be projected by moving one or both upper extremities
rapidly, transferring this momentum to an object, and then releasing the object, allowing its inertia to move it until gravity pulls it to earth and/or friction stops its motion. This type of task is called *rolling* if the object is released
along the surface or *throwing* if it is released so that it is projected into the air.
Many different movements may be used to roll or throw an object depending on
the specific purpose of the action. However, there are certain principles that
determine the efficiency of the movements. The purpose of the specific task
determines the movements that best apply each principle. The speed of the
object at release is the same as the speed of movement of the hand(s)
holding the object. Speed of movement of the distal end of any body segment
depends upon the time and distance over which the momentum can be developed, the speed of the muscular contraction, the length of the lever being
moved, the number of body segments involved, and the sequence of the
action.

The distance for the development of momentum is increased by lengthening the backswing. Thus when maximum speed of an object is desired, the
hand is carried backward as far as possible through action of the arm and
shoulder, trunk rotation, and transference of weight to the back foot. Obviously, the faster the muscles are contracted the faster the body segments
move, and when maximum speed is desired the muscles are contracted as
rapidly as possible. Since the longer the lever the faster its distal end moves
for a given movement at the joint, maximum speed results from combining
many segments of the body into a system of levers. To gain maximum speed
of the final lever, each must be brought into the action at the point when
the segment below is moving at its maximum speed. This is known as
"sequential action." In an overhand throw (right-handed thrower) the rotation to the left starts in the pelvis and as this gains speed the trunk rotation begins. When it reaches its top speed, shoulder girdle action begins,

followed by the elbow, wrist, and fingers, each coming into action at the time the preceding segment is moving at its fastest. This combining of segments also results in the use of more muscles and thus contributes to the production of more force.

Since it is the speed of the hand(s) *at the moment of release* that determines the speed of the object, the fastest throw or roll results from a release which coincides with the moment when the hand is moving its fastest. It is impossible to stop a movement instantaneously. It requires time and distance to decelerate just as it requires time and distance to build up momentum. Thus the greatest speed of the object results when it is released near the center of the arc of the movement. While the follow-through of a movement takes place after the object has been released, it affects the object because of its effect on the movement which precedes the release.

When less than maximum speed is required by the task, various of the above factors may be modified; the degree of modification depends on the proportion of maximum force required. The way in which the factors are modified depends upon the individual. One may choose to reduce force by cutting the length of the backswing, by doing away with trunk rotation, another by lessening the arm and shoulder action. Or the force may be reduced by slowing the muscular contraction. No two individuals adjust in exactly the same way. The important thing is that all understand the principles involved so that each can make the applications required by the purpose of each particular task.

Because body segments are moving, the center of gravity of the body is shifting and the balance principles (see discussion of supportive tasks, pp. 37–42) must be considered. In order to keep the center of gravity of the body above the base, the base needs to be enlarged in the same direction as the force is applied, since that is the direction in which the center of gravity moves (Fig. 28). However, *the degree of adjustment* of the base also depends upon the way in which those factors that produce speed of the throwing hand(s)—and thus the force given the object—are modified to effect various purposes. In general the enlarging of the base should be accomplished by placing the foot opposite to the throwing hand forward so that the resultant rotation of the pelvis contributes to, rather than restricts, trunk rotation during the backswing. When the particular task requires very little force, trunk rotation is not demanded and it is perfectly possible that the individual might prefer to enlarge the base slightly with the same foot as throwing hand, forward. This position removes the restriction of rotation during follow-through and thus may contribute to accuracy. However, since the rotation of both pelvis and shoulder girdle is to the left it may cause a tendency for movement to be toward the left rather than forward and this must be controlled. If the *reasons* for placing the opposite foot forward are thoroughly understood the individual can make intelligent judgments as to when it is necessary to the efficiency of the throwing or rolling movement (4).

Whenever the foot is placed forward of the center of gravity it pushes *forward*-downward against the surface which applies a reaction force *backward*-upward to the body. This resists the forward movement of the body. This resistive force, inherent in the forward foot, can be removed by allowing the forward knee to bend as the body moves forward over the base.

In a rolling task the bend of the forward knee makes an added contribution to the efficiency of the total movement. A rolling task presents the

FIG. 28.

Throw. Step forward to enlarge the base under the forward moving center of gravity.

added problem of lowering the hand so that the object can be released along the surface. The lowering of the hand must be accomplished without upsetting the balance of the body. The center of gravity can be kept above the base and lowered for increased stability by bending the hips, knees, and ankles as the arm is swung forward. Leaning forward from the hips to lower the hand leaves the center of gravity high and forward, and the body is more easily pulled off balance by the movement of the arm. If the hand is not lowered and the ball is released above the surface it gains downward momentum as gravity pulls it down and it hits the surface with downward force as well as the forward force which was applied by the hand. This results in upward force being applied by the surface to the object and it bounces, how high depends upon the height of release above the surface, and the degree of restitution of the object (its ability to retake its shape after being flattened by impact). This forceful contact with the floor (downward force) increases the friction and reduces the forward momentum. Also it may change the direction of the path of the object.

Because an object tends to continue to move in the direction that it is moving until acted upon by another force (inertia), the object moves in the direction that the hand was moving at the moment of release. Therefore, the direction of the object can only be controlled by controlling the direction of the movement of the hand(s). If the hand is moving in an arc at the instant of release, the object leaves the hand in a direction that is tangent

FIG. 29.

Movement of shoulder forward and downward which slightly flattens arc of hand in underhand throw.

to that arc. This is the direction the hand was moving at that instant. Since the arm (and all other body segments) moves around a joint, the hand moves in an arc. The flatter an arc the less divergent are the tangents at various points on the arc (5). Thus anything that flattens the arc of the hand contributes to the control of the direction of the object. In rolling or throwing underhand, stepping forward onto a bent knee moves the shoulder (the center of the arc made by the hand) both forward, in the direction of the movement, and downward, somewhat flattening the arc through which the hand moves and increasing the possibility for a throw at the desired angle (Fig. 29). The sequential action of the segments of the arm in the overhand throw contributes to a flatter arc. Right to left accuracy is difficult to control when throwing with a sidearm movement pattern because the arc of movement is from side to side. The forward step or weight transference helps to flatten the arc to some degree.

Follow-through contributes to accuracy as well as speed because it increases the possibilities that the hand will be traveling in the direction of desired movement *at the moment of release.* An attempt to stop the movement at, or right after, release results in a jerking of the hand and arm and the path of the object cannot be predicted.

In throwing, the tendency of the object to move in the direction that the hand was moving at release is modified by gravity. At release two forces are acting on the object. One is the force produced by the moving hand giving the object momentum in the direction the hand was moving at release and

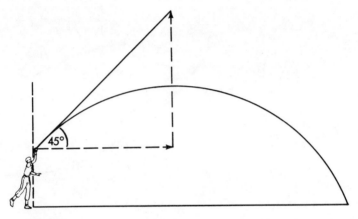

45°

FIG. 30.

Path of ball thrown at 45 degree angle. Half of force effective upward and half effective forward (air resistance neglected).

the other is gravity accelerating the object in a downward direction. The object moves in the direction which is the resultant of these two forces. The length of time an object remains in the air *if given no upward or downward force by the hand* depends upon the height of release. If the hand is moving forward-upward at release, a portion of the force produced by the body is upward and resists gravity's pull. The object, therefore, remains in the air longer than if projected straight outward. Of course, if the hand is moving forward-downward at release, a portion of the force is downward and is added to the force of gravity making the object drop more rapidly. When the hand is moving forward-upward at an angle of 45 degrees to the surface, half of the body force is applied upward to resist gravity and half forward to send the object forward (Fig. 30). A release at a higher angle (greater than 45 degrees) results in a greater proportion of the force being applied upward and the ball remains in the air longer but since it is given less forward force, it does not travel as far. A release at an angle lower than 45 degrees applies the greater proportion of force forward but the ball does not stay in the air long enough to take full advantage of this force. When air resistance is not a problem the 45 degree angle is the most effective angle of release *if distance is the objective of the throw*. It keeps the object in the air long enough to gain the full benefit of the forward force. If speed is the objective the lowest angle that will keep the ball in the air long enough for it to travel the required distance should be used. Time is wasted in sending the ball in a higher arc.

Of course, air resistance is encountered by any object moving through the air and it gradually slows the forward motion of the object. It varies with the size of the surface area and the weight and speed of the object. The greater the area of the surface moving through the air, the greater the resistance of the air to the movement of the object. However, the heavier the object the greater its momentum (momentum equals speed times mass); therefore the greater the force the object exerts against the air and the less effective the air resistance in slowing the object. Air resistance increases greatly as speed increases. If the speed of a ball is doubled, its momentum is doubled but air resistance is *quadrupled*. Therefore, a relatively heavy ball traveling at a moderate speed (basketball) is little affected by air resistance. Pitched baseballs or softballs which travel much faster are more affected. Also, in this case the combination of spin and air resistance is important.

If in releasing the ball an off-center force is applied or the ball is rotated, it will continue to rotate (spin). When a ball is spinning forward (that is, the top of the ball is moving in the same direction as the ball is moving), the air carried around the ball as it spins is moving forward on top of the ball and meets resistance at the top forward edge of the ball. This flow of air forward over the top of the ball is in opposition to the wall of air into which the ball is moving. Air pressure builds up at this point. The air below the ball is moving backward since the bottom of the ball is moving backward, and the pressure below the ball is decreased. Thus a ball with forward (top) spin tends to drop more rapidly than one with no spin. It follows that a ball with back spin (top of the ball moving away from the direction in which the ball is moving) carries air around it which moves backward on top of the ball and forward under the ball. This results in pressure decreasing above the ball and building up under the front of the bottom of the ball and this pressure, being in opposition to gravity, tends to keep the ball in the air longer.

Also, at release a ball can be started rotating to the right or left. When the *front* of the ball (the side facing the direction of movement) is moving right and the back (side toward thrower) is moving left, the ball has right spin. When the front is moving toward the thrower's left, it has left spin. These spins carry a layer of air around the ball horizontally and cause pressure areas on the sides of the ball which modify its direction. A ball spinning to the right carries air backward on its right side and forward on its left, and therefore the pressure builds up on the left, drops on the right, and the ball curves to the right. The left spinning ball carries air backward on the left side and forward on the right, building the pressure on the right, reducing it on the left, and it curves left. Since air resistance increases rapidly as speed increases, spin causes more change in the direction of a fast than a slow ball, and the faster the spin the greater its effect. However, the effect of the spin is seen later in the flight of a fast moving ball. It does not become noticeable until the forward momentum has been somewhat reduced by the effect of air resistance. Anything that increases the air resistance to the flight of a ball (such as a headwind) increases the change in the direction of the ball as a result of spin.

A ball with no spin may curve if its seams are in unequal positions on the two sides (6). This position results in uneven air pressure on the two sides and the direction of the ball can not be predicted. Because spin has a stabilizing effect on the flight of the ball some spin is desirable. Whether it is top spin, back spin, or side spin depends upon the specific purpose of the activity (7).

Normally air resistance is less of a factor modifying the motion of a rolled object than a thrown object but friction is a greater factor. In fact, friction is a factor in throwing only in tasks requiring a *roll* after the object has dropped to the surface. Friction acts in opposition to the forward force and therefore slows the rolling movement. In rolling, the amount of friction depends mainly upon the two surfaces involved. The harder the ball and the surface over which it rolls, the less the rolling friction. A ball which is rolling forward pushes backward against the surface and friction results in an opposite (forward) force on the ball. This force is added to the forward force given the ball at the time of release, and therefore increases the speed of the roll. If the ball is spinning backward when released along a surface, the ball pushes forward against the surface which pushes the ball backward and this, being in opposition to the forward motion, slows the ball. If the back spin force is slight, friction overcomes this force quickly, reversing the spin and causing the ball to roll in the direction of movement. If it is great, the ball slides along the surface until the friction overcomes the spin force and the slowed ball begins to roll forward. A rolling ball with left spin curves left and right spin curves right.

sudden application of force

Another method for projecting objects is called striking. Objects may be struck by a body segment or by an implement controlled by the body. Throwing and striking tasks require basically the same movement patterns (8). They differ in that when throwing the momentum of a body segment(s) is imparted to an object *held* by the segment (usually the upper extremity) and released, while in striking, force is imparted through a momentary contact with the object. Momentum of the body segment(s) is developed in the same way for both types of tasks. However, in striking tasks the distal end of the lever imparting the force is not restricted to a body segment or implement that can hold an object in contact while the momentum is being developed. Therefore, many parts of the body can be used as the striking surface (for example, the head, shoulder, knee, foot in soccer; the foot in football; the hand(s) in volleyball and handball, etc.). Also, the striking lever can be

FIG. 31.

Comparison of length of arcs through which racket and hand move.

lengthened considerably by use of some implement. In a given time, the distance through which the end of the striking implement moves is much greater than that through which the hand moves, thus increasing the speed potential of striking tasks (Fig. 31). Lacrosse does employ an instrument to lengthen the throwing lever but there are relatively few such throwing activities. On the other hand, leverage is applied to increase the speed of the object imparting the force in a wide variety of striking tasks. The many sport rackets, paddles, bats and clubs, the axe, the sledge hammer, the scythe, and even the fly swatter are all implements that lengthen the striking lever and thus increase the speed potential. The lengthened lever arm, however, makes control more difficult since the force of impact is taken at a greater distance from the axis for the movement. For example, the head of the long golf club travels at a high speed but requires great control to assure that the striking surface at impact is facing the direction of desired movement of the ball. In addition, the long-handled axe has greater potential force, but the short-handled hatchet is easier to control. Which implement is chosen depends upon the force required for the purpose and the strength of the individual using it.

Also, lengthening the striking lever may cause a problem of spatial orientation. While an individual is able to judge accurately and instantaneously the distance he can reach with his hand, he must learn through experience the distances he can reach with various implements. The player who is inexperienced in using a racket tends to run to the position from which he could reach the ball with his hand and, at the last minute, must adjust his swing by pulling the elbow in toward his body, thus interfering with the

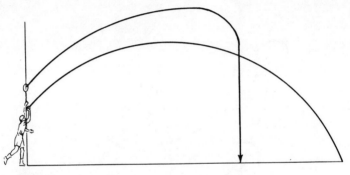

FIG. 32.

Path of shuttle compared to path of ball which encounters little air resistance. (Adapted from Broer, Marion R., *Efficiency of Human Movement*. Philadelphia: W. B. Saunders, 1966, p. 102.)

timing and direction of the swing as well as losing the potential force of the longer lever.

The influence of air resistance is usually greater in striking than in throwing tasks because of the greater speed that can be imparted through use of the longer lever. In fact, air resistance may be so great that the forward motion of the object is stopped before gravity has had time to pull the object to earth. This can be noted in the flight of a badminton shuttle which is less compact than a ball, is very light, and can be projected at great speed (Fig. 32). The effect of spin tends to be greater in striking tasks also because the greater speed of the object increases the air resistance. The decided curve in the flight of a golf ball given side spin is well known to anyone who has had any experience with golf.

When force is applied by striking, the inertia of the object must be overcome instantaneously. At impact the struck object applies a reaction force to the striking implement. To assure the application of maximum force to the object the striking implement must be firm so that it does not "give" with this force of impact. If the striking surface gives, less force is applied to the object, since some is absorbed in the "giving." This means that the surface itself must be firm, and it must not be allowed to move backward as a result of the force of impact. The flat hand with its many small bones does not afford a firm surface for striking. However, there are various methods for making the hand a firmer surface and these are used in volleyball and handball. A tennis racket may be allowed to move backward at contact because the wrist muscles have not been contracted sufficiently or because they lack the strength to withstand this force so far away from the axis (distance from shoulder to center of racket). This results in a loss of direction as well as force since it angles the racket face toward the right (right-handed player). The bunt in baseball makes use of a "giving" of the implement for the purpose of reducing the force applied to the ball.

In striking tasks the degree of restitution of the object being struck is also important. The faster that the object, compressed by the sudden application of force, retakes its original shape, the faster it moves away from the striking implement. Thus an old tennis ball that has lost some of its ability to bounce moves with less speed than a new ball hit with the same force.

The law of rebound, which states that in general an object rebounds from a solid surface at an angle equal to that at which it approached the surface, operates in striking tasks. The angle is modified by any give in the striking surface or in the ball unless the ball immediately retakes its original shape. Thus, an old tennis ball rebounds at a lower angle than it approaches the court and any tennis ball rebounds at a lower angle from a grass than a clay or hard surface court.

Spin also affects this angle of rebound. When a spinning ball strikes a surface two forces are involved, the force of impact and the force imparted to the striking surface by the ball as it turns (spins). The rebound is the resultant of these two forces. When a horizontal surface is involved, the bottom of the ball with top spin (moving backward) pushes backward against the surface; thus the reaction force from the surface against the ball is forward. The resultant of this forward force and the force of impact is at a lower angle than the angle equal to the angle of approach. If a ball with no spin were dropped straight down on the floor it would rebound straight up. If this ball had top (forward) spin it would rebound in the direction of the resultant of the forward force caused by the floor's reaction to the backward push by the bottom of the ball and the upward force from the impact. In other words, it would rebound at a forward-upward angle, or at an angle between the two forces—the one upward and the one forward. If this ball had back spin it would rebound in the direction of the resultant of a *backward* force caused by the floor's reaction to the forward push by the bottom of the ball and the upward force from impact. This resultant would be at a backward-upward angle.

A ball with no spin approaching a horizontal surface at an angle rebounds forward at an equal angle. If this ball had top spin the resultant of the spin and impact forces would again be somewhere between the normal (no spin) rebound and straight forward. This means the *angle* of rebound would be less than that of a ball without spin. The rebound of a ball with back spin would be between the normal rebound and straight backward. This means the angle between the ball's flight and the floor would be greater than normal (no spin). How much the spin changes the angle of rebound depends upon the speed of the spin relative to the force of the impact. A fast spin in combination with a relatively light impact results in a considerable change in the rebound; a slower spin in combination with a forceful impact results in little change in rebound from the normal.

If a ball that is spinning to the right * is thrown straight downward it rebounds straight upward. Because the front of the ball is moving to the right and the back is moving left, two equal and opposite forces are exerted against the floor and the reaction forces neutralize each other (9). The same is true of a left spinning ball. However, if a ball with right spin strikes the floor *at an angle* the direction of the *back* of the bottom of the ball determines the effect of the spin. Because the back of a right spinning ball is moving left, the ball pushes against the floor to the left and the ball rebounds at an angle *between* straight ahead (impact force) and straight right (reaction force of floor to the spin force)—or forward-right. Again how far to the right the ball bounces depends on the relative force of the impact and the spin. The left spinning ball bounces forward-left. Because it is the bottom of the ball that contacts a *horizontal* surface, the direction of movement of the *bottom* of the ball determines the direction of the *spin force,* and the reaction force *affecting* the *ball* is in the *opposite direction*. It is the direction of movement of the *back of the bottom* of the ball which is important when a ball with side spin hits the floor at an angle.

When a *vertical striking surface,* such as a tennis racket or basketball backboard rather than a horizontal surface such as the floor, is involved the *front* of the ball (as it moves into the racket) contacts the surface. The front of the ball with top spin is moving downward and it pushes downward on the surface. Thus the ball is pushed more upward than normal (Fig. 33). The front of a ball with back spin pushes upward and thus the ball falls more rapidly. The front of the right spinning ball pushes to the right and the reaction force pushes it left so it rebounds more left. Similarly, the left

---

* This discussion considers side spin around a vertical axis only. For a more detailed discussion of the effect of spin on angle of rebound, the reader is referred to Ref. 10.

spinning ball pushes left and rebounds more right. It is the direction of movement of the *front* of the ball which gives the direction of the spin force *against a vertical* surface. The reaction force affecting the ball is, of course, in the opposite direction.

Striking activities may involve a moving ball hitting a solid surface, a moving instrument hitting a stationary ball, or a moving instrument contacting a moving ball. When a moving ball strikes the floor or a basketball backstop, for example, the force of its impact (a variable dependent upon the object's speed, its degree of restitution, and the firmness of the surface), the angle of this impact, and any spin on the ball affect the path of its rebound. All of these factors have been discussed previously.

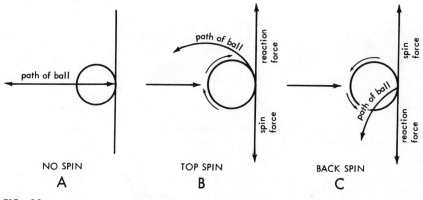

FIG. 33.

Effect of spin on rebound from vertical surface. A. Ball with no spin. B. Ball with forward spin rebounds higher than normal. C. Ball with back spin rebounds lower than normal.

When a moving instrument strikes a stationary ball, the speed and weight of the implement, the firmness of the striking surface, the angle of the striking surface and the direction that it is moving, the point at which it contacts the object, and the object's ability to retake its shape rapidly are all factors in determining the path of the object. The speed of the instrument is dependent upon the many factors covered in the discussion of throwing as well as on the length of the implement, also previously covered. However, the force is dependent upon the total momentum of the implement and therefore, its weight is also important (momentum equals *mass* times velocity). Because of its greater weight the tennis racket has more inherent force than the lighter badminton racket. However, this additional weight makes it harder to control, and unless the wrist muscles are strong, wrist action cannot be used effectively. Since the badminton racket is light, even relatively weak wrist muscles can manipulate it with ease. This makes it possible to move the badminton racket through a greater distance very rapidly just at the moment of contact. Thus the speed of the badminton racket can compensate for its lack of weight.

If the striking surface is not firm or if the object does not retake its shape rapidly following its flattening by the force of impact, some of the force of impact is dissipated; thus the object is projected with less speed and the angle of rebound is modified.

The angle of the striking surface determines the angle between the object and the surface at impact and therefore the angle of rebound. Two forces are involved in the projection. One, the force caused by the momentum of the striking implement, operates in the direction the implement is moving at the moment of contact (tangent to the arc of movement). The other is the rebound force, which is in the direction of an angle equal and opposite

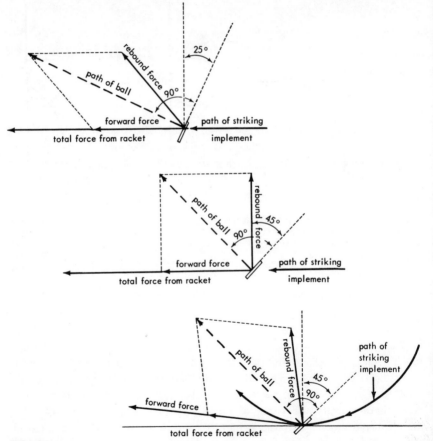

FIG. 34.

Striking stationary ball. Path of ball at right angles to striking surface. (Adapted from Broer, Marion R., *Efficiency of Human Movement*. Philadelphia: W. B. Saunders, 1966, p. 235.)

to the angle of impact. The object is projected in a direction which is the resultant of these two forces. When the object is stationary both of these forces are derived from the motion of the striking implement and half of the force is applied in the direction of its motion and half in the direction of the rebound; therefore the resultant is half way between the two. This results in a projection which is at right angles to the striking surface (Fig. 34).

If an object is contacted off center, so that the line from the point of contact to the center of the ball is not in the direction in which the striking surface is moving, the ball is given spin and the direction of force can no longer be predicted from the direction of movement of the striking surface and the angle of its face. A ball hit with a forward force but contacted above the center of gravity is given forward spin and a forward-downward force. One hit below its center of gravity is given back spin and an upward-forward force. How much these forces send the ball down or up depends upon how far from the center of the back of the ball the force is applied.

When a moving striking surface contacts a moving ball, all of the above factors are involved, and in addition, the momentum (weight and speed) of the *object,* its direction of approach to the striking surface, and any spin affect the direction of projection. In any striking situation the total momentum after impact equals the total momentum before impact (Law of Conservation of Momentum). "In other words, when a bat meets an oncoming ball the total resulting momentum is the sum of the momentum of the bat (the weight of the bat times its speed) and the momentum of the ball (the weight of the ball times its speed). The difference between the two determines the direction of the resulting motion. It is in the direction of the greater momentum" (11).

The direction of approach of the object as well as the angle of the striking surface are involved in the direction of the rebound force *and,* if the ball is spinning, this is an additional factor. The relative importance of these variables depends upon the relationship between the momentum of the striking instrument and the momentum of the oncoming object. If the momentum of the striking instrument is great in relation to that of the object, its direction of movement and the angle of its surface are much more important in determining the path of the ball than are the direction of approach and spin of the ball. However, when the momentum of the ball is great in relation to that of the instrument, the ball direction and spin affect considerably the direction of the ball after impact.

indirect application of force

The human body can cause objects to move by applying force indirectly; that is, the body can move some other object into a position so that it in turn can supply the force to move the object. The body action involved in these tasks is essentially a push or pull. The string of a bow is pulled back bending the bow into a curved position giving it potential energy. When the force of the body which maintains this position is released, the bow retakes its shape applying forward force to the arrow through the string. The same principles are involved in the use of a sling shot. A pull on the trigger of a gun releases the hammer which strikes a bullet and projects it from the gun. Since the body action for this type of task is either a pull or push the principles for pushing and pulling objects discussed earlier apply.

REFERENCES

1. Broer, Marion R. *Efficiency of Human Movement.* Philadelphia: W. B. Saunders Company, 1966, p. 359.
2. *Ibid.,* p. 257.
3. *Ibid.,* p. 4.
4. *Ibid.,* pp. 212–13.
5. See discussion of throwing, *Ibid.,* pp. 213–15.
6. Hicks, Clifford B. "The Strange Forces of the Air," *Popular Mechanics Magazine,* 111:6:127 (June 1959).
7. For a complete description of spin see Broer, *Efficiency of Human Movement,* pp. 83–93.
8. *Ibid.,* pp. 6–21.
9. *Ibid.,* pp. 88–89.
10. *Ibid.,* pp. 87–93, 230–34, 244–45.
11. *Ibid.,* p. 225.

TASKS INVOLVING
RECEIVING FORCE

Many tasks involve the stopping of movement, either that of the body itself or of an object. Any time that the moving body contacts a surface or a moving object contacts the body, the surface or the object exerts a force against the body (Newton's Third Law—Action-Reaction). The way in which this force is received determines whether injury to the body results and, in the case of an object, whether the object rebounds from the body. Whether the task requires catching a ball or some other object; landing from a fall (body weight out of control), a jump, a leap, or even a step in a run; or entering the water with a dive or a jump; the force of impact must be dissipated gradually. If the motion is stopped suddenly all of the force is exerted at once and the reaction force may cause injury and/or rebound. Landing from a VERY SMALL jump causes considerable jarring of the entire body if the hips, knees, and ankles are kept rigid as the feet hit the floor. On the other hand, if the hips, knees, and ankles are allowed to flex as the feet contact the floor, little or no jarring occurs even when landing from a considerably higher jump. Since the acceleration caused by gravity increases rapidly, an increase in the vertical distance the body drops greatly increases the force of impact. In landing from a jump the momentum can be slowed gradually by bending the joints of the lower extremities. Some force is exerted against the surface as the feet make contact, but because of the controlled bending of the joints of the legs (which allows the body to keep moving but gradually slows the momentum), there is little jar. This controlled bending is commonly called "giving," and the gradual stoppage of the movement is known as "force absorption."

When a moving ball is contacted by hands held firm against the impact, the ball rebounds and the force of impact is felt in the hands. Unless the momentum of a ball is reduced gradually so that only a small portion of the force it exerts against the hand(s) is returned to it at any given point in time, the force tends to cause the ball to reverse its direction rapidly (rebound) and thus it is difficult or impossible to maintain contact with it. However, if the momentum is reduced gradually by moving the hands in the direction the ball is moving—resisting its movement with a force only sufficient to slow the motion gradually—contact can be maintained easily. If the purpose of the task involves projecting the ball with the hands, the hands should be as solid as possible to assure that the total force inherent in the contact is transferred back to the ball. However, if the purpose of the task is to maintain control of the ball, the force of impact must be gradually absorbed. This is accomplished by reaching forward to contact the ball so that there is space through which the hands can be moved in the direction of the ball's motion after the moment of contact; thus the ball is allowed to continue to move toward the body and its momentum is stopped gradually. The ball can be allowed to move even farther by a transference of the body weight from the forward to the back foot or, when it is moving very fast, by taking a step backward. The faster the ball is moving when contacted, the longer the time required to stop its momentum gradually and the greater the distance the hands will have to move in the direction of the ball's movement.

Normally when jumping, the body is under control and lands on the feet; absorption of the force can be accomplished by flexing the joints of the lower extremities. Actually momentum and gravity will bend the hips, knees, and ankles if the individual does not contract the extensors to the extent that he prevents this from taking place. Frequently when the task involves the absorption of any degree of force, it is performed on a partially nonresistive surface such as a mat. When considerable force is involved in the impact, a jumping pit (filled with soft material), which slows the momentum over a longer distance and time, is used. Any nonresistive surface allows for gradual force absorption both by the surface and the body and thus provides greater reduction of the jar of impact.

The body does not always land on its feet and the momentum cannot always be brought under voluntary control. However, there are many ways in which the body's momentum can be stopped gradually in order to reduce the force of the impact. Anything that can be done to make the body into an object that can roll instead of hitting flat, will result in a more gradual loss of momentum and thus less injury. When falling forward or sideways the upper extremities can assist in absorbing some of the force of impact and also in redirecting it. The body can be tucked into a ball (more or less) and the hands and arms, after gradually absorbing some force by controlled giving, can transfer the weight to the back of the rounded shoulders or the rounded back so that the body will continue to roll. When falling backward the body is less able to absorb the force of impact gradually.

Regardless of the task involving the stopping of momentum, the problem is to determine a way in which the force of impact can be absorbed gradually if the moving body or object is to be stopped without injury to the body. The greater the force of impact the longer the time required to absorb the force gradually. If the purpose of the task is to make use of the force of impact to project an oncoming object, the segment of the body making contact should be held firmly so that it is a solid surface with no give.

The second vital consideration is the size of the area of contact. The force with which the moving body or object contacts a surface is distributed over the entire surface contacted. If a large surface area is involved, the force is spread and the amount of force that must be taken by any one unit of the area may not be great. However if this *same* force of impact is applied against a surface *half as large,* the amount of force that must be taken by each unit of the area is *twice* as great. While no injury results from contacting a ball travelling at a given speed when the area of both palms is used, this same force applied against the small end of a finger results in considerable injury to that finger. Not only is the entire force concentrated on a very small area but also the force is in the direction which jams the bones of the finger against each other and this is an additional factor causing injury (1). If the force of impact of the falling body is taken on an elbow or knee (small area with no give), injury is more likely than when taken on a larger and more padded area of the body.

The problems involved in those tasks in which the body contacts a *nonresistive* surface (one that will part and allow the body to move through) are different from those in which it contacts a resistive surface. While a jumping pit is nonresistive to a degree, it does not allow the body to pass through it as does water. To cut through a cake, the smallest possible surface of the knife blade (the edge) is used. If the flat side of the blade were pressed against the cake, it would resist the passage of the knife. In the same way the body passes easily through the water surface if the small area of the finger tips contact the surface, but if the body lands flat on its back, the force of impact resisting passage of the body through the water is great.

If in diving, the elbows are allowed to bend as the hands contact the water they will not part the water particles, and the full force of the impact will be taken on the larger surface area of the head. Since the purpose of diving is to cut through the water, the smallest surface area of the body should make contact and the body should be kept rigid (2). Thus the principles for diving into water (nonresistive) are the opposite of those for falling or landing on a resistive surface. A nonresistive surface parts and slows the body momentum gradually because of water friction. A resistive surface, as the name implies, stops the body's motion suddenly; therefore, the gradual absorption of the force of impact must be accomplished by the body itself. In some cases where the surface is partially nonresistive (jumping pit), both the surface and the body absorb the force.

If the purpose is to jump into the water and keep the head from going under water (life saving technique), the legs are spread forward-backward to increase the area of contact front-to-back and the arms are held out to the sides at shoulder height to increase the area side-to-side. The force of the water against this large area resists the movement of the body through the water. Since the surface area is not as great as when the body lands flat on its back, the momentum is not stopped as suddenly and the force of impact is not sufficient to cause injury, only to stop the downward momentum more rapidly—hopefully, before the head goes below the surface.

Many force absorption tasks do not involve actual contact. One that is rarely discussed as such, but is very common, is that of stopping the motion of a rapidly moving body segment. When a segment of the body is moved, the force of its inertia (tendency to keep moving at that speed and in that direction) must be overcome to stop its motion. If the movement is slow so that the inertia is slight the motion may be overcome by gravity alone. However, when the movement is very fast or the segment is moving downward, muscular effort is required in addition and its inertia must be overcome gradually to avoid injury and/or loss of control. For example, when throwing or striking the arm is moving very fast at the moment the ball is released or struck and it takes time and distance to absorb its momentum gradually. This is one purpose of the follow-through. If there were no follow-through, stopping the momentum would have to begin *before* the release or impact, and maximum speed could not be transferred to the object; thus force of projection would be lost. But the follow-through gives time and distance for a gradual stoppage of the movement *after* the point of release or impact, thus making it possible to accelerate *until* the point of release or impact in order to impart the greatest possible force.

In all force absorption tasks, balance of the body is a problem to be considered, and the balance principles discussed earlier must be applied. The most important of these principles for such tasks involves the widening of the base in the direction of the force of impact or of the body motion that must be stopped.

REFERENCES

1. Broer, Marion R. *Efficiency of Human Movement.* Philadelphia: W. B. Saunders Company, 1966, p. 220.

2. *Ibid.,* p. 161.

Index

Abdominal muscles, 32 (*see also* Muscles)
Achilles tendon, 19
Acromion process, 24
Action-Reaction law (*see* Newton's Third Law of Motion)
Air resistance, in moving of objects, 73–74 (*see also* Objects, moving of)
Anatomy, of human body, 6–9
Archimedes' principle, 42
Arms, 26
Attitudinal reactions, 10–15 (*see also* Reflexes)

Balance principles, 69, 87
Basmajian, S. V., 23
Beevoir, C., 28
Body projecting activities, 60–62
Body righting reflexes, 13 (*see also* Reflexes)
Bones, 6–7 (*also throughout*)
Brain, 8–9 (*see also* Nervous system)
Broer, M. R., 2, 3, 28, 40, 80, 82, 87
Bunnell, Sterling, 28
Buoyancy, force of, 42

Campbell, E. J. M., 33
Capener, Norman, 28
Carpal bones, 26–27
Cartilage, 6
Center of gravity, defined, 37
Center of gravity shifts, 21, 22, 51–62 (*also throughout*)
Children:
  gastrocnemius muscle, 19
  reflexes, 10, 11, 12, 13–14, 15 (*see also* Reflexes)
  suspension tasks, 47
Clavicle, 24
Close, J. R., 23

Codman, E. A., 29
Contraction, of muscles, 7–9 (*see also* Muscles)
Coracoid process, 24
Cortex, of human brain, 8–9 (*see also* Nervous system)
Cranium, 31
Crossed extension reflex, 12 (*see also* Reflexes)

Definitions, of kinesiology, 1–3
Deltoid muscle, 25 (*see also* Muscles)
Dempster, W. T., 29
Diaphragm muscles, 32
Distance jumping, 60–62
Diving, 15, 83, 86
"The Dual Sensory Role of Muscle Spindles," 11
Duchenne, G. B. A., 33
Dynamic position, 33

Ear:
  internal, 14–15
  labyrinthine reflexes, 14–15
  semicircular canals, 41
  vestibular organ, 14–15
Elbows, 26
Eldred, Earl, 11
Electromyographic studies, 2, 21
Exercises, positions in, 54–56
Extensor muscles, spine, 32
Extremities, lower, 17–22
Extremities, upper, 24–28
Eye-hand coordination, 33
Eyes, 15, 33

Face bones, 31
Facial expressions, 31

Fatigue, problem of, 3
Feet, 17–18, 19, 21
"Fencing stance," 13
Fingers, 26–27, 28
First Law of Motion, Newton's, 50–51
Fischer, F. J., 23
Flatt, A., 29
Flexor digitorum longus muscle, 19 (*see also* Muscles)
Floyd, W. F., 33
Follow-through movements, 72, 86 (*see also* Objects, moving of)
Force, sudden application of, 74–81
Force absorption tasks, 83–87
Force of buoyancy, 42
Force of gravity, 36–37 (*also throughout*)
Force of impact, 83–87
Forces, indirect, 81–82 (*see also* Objects, moving of)
Forward movements, 60
Friction, in moving of objects, 62–63, 65, 74
Friction, in running and walking, 58
Fulton, J. F., 7, 9, 16

Gala, R., 48, 49
Gastrocnemius muscle, 19, 21
Gellhorn, E., 8, 9
General static reactions, 12–15 (*see also* Reflexes)
"Giving," in force receiving, 84
Gluteus maximus muscle, 18, 21
Gooddy, W., 8, 9
Gravity, force of, 36–37 (*also throughout*)

Hagbarth, K. E., 23
Hamstring muscle, 19, 21, 26 (*see also* Muscles)
Hand function, 26–28
Hands, in striking, 77 (*see also* Objects, moving of)
Head movements, 12–15, 30–33
Hellebrandt, F. A., 13, 16, 39, 46
Hicks, Clifford B., 82
Hip extension, 17, 21
Houtz, S. J., 2, 3, 23, 28
Howorth, M. B., 33
Human body, as lever system, 54–56
Humerus, 24–25, 26

Iliopsoas, 18–19 (*see also* Muscles)
Impact, force of, 83–87
Inertia, Law of, 50
Infants (*see* Children)
"Inhibition in the Central Nervous System," 11
Intercostal muscles, 32 (*see also* Muscles)

Internal ear, 14–15 (*see also* Middle ear; Semicircular canals)
Isometric contraction, 7
Isotonic contraction, 7

Jones, F. W., 23
Jonsson, B., 23
Joseph, J., 23
Jumping, 60–62, 83–85
Jumping pits, 84, 85

Kabat, H., 9
Kamon, E., 25–26, 29
Karlsson, E., 23
Kinesiology, defined, 1–3
Knee, flexion and extension, 17
Knee jerk, 11 (*see also* Reflexes)
Kugelberg, E., 23

Labyrinthine reflexes, 14–15 (*see also* Internal ear; Middle ear; Semicircular canals)
Landau reflex, 15 (*see also* Reflexes)
Law of Conservation of Momentum, 81 (*see also* Objects, moving of)
Law of Inertia, 50
Legs, 26
"Lengthening contraction," 7
Leverage, in moving of objects, 63, 67–68 (*see also* Objects, moving of)
Leverage principles, in supportive tasks, 44–45
Leverage system, of body, 54–56
Lifting, of objects, 66–67 (*see also* Objects, moving of)
Ligaments, 7
Line of gravity, defined, 37
Linear motion, 51
Local static reactions, 11 (*see also* Reflexes)
Long, C., 29
Long distance jumping, 60–62
Lower extremities, 17–22
Lucas, D. B., 29

Magnus, R., 10, 13, 15, 16
Mechanism, for body movement, 6–33
Middle ear, 41 (*see also* Labyrinthine reflexes; Semicircular canals)
Momentum, Law of Conservation of, 81
Momentum and release, of objects, 68–74 (*see also* Objects, moving of)
Monosynaptic reflex, 11–12 (*see also* Reflexes)
Morton, J. Dudley, 46
Motion, First Law of, 50–51
Motion, Second Law of, 51, 57
Motion, Third Law of, 56, 83